MANAGEMENT SCIENCES IN THE EMERGING COUNTRIES

MANAGEMENT SCIENCES IN THE EMERGING COUNTRIES

New Tools for Economic Development

EDITED BY

Norman N. Barish
Michel Verhulst

PERGAMON PRESS

OXFORD · LONDON · EDINBURGH · NEW YORK

PARIS · FRANKFURT

Pergamon Press Ltd., Headington Hill Hall, Oxford
4 & 5 Fitzroy Square, London W.1
Pergamon Press (Scotland) Ltd., 2 & 3 Teviot Place, Edinburgh 1
Pergamon Press Inc., 122 East 55th St., New York 22, N.Y.
Gauthier-Villars, 55 Quai des Grands-Augustins, Paris 6
Pergamon Press GmbH, Kaiserstrasse 75, Frankfurt-am-Main

First edition 1965

Library of Congress Catalog Card No. 63–18929

PRINTED IN GREAT BRITAIN BY THE ALDEN PRESS, OXFORD

CONTENTS

PART TWO   RESOURCE ALLOCATION DECISIONS

PART THREE   CASE EXPERIMENTS AND APPLICATIONS

PREFACE

THE contents of this volume are drawn primarily from the papers presented at a symposium which the College on Managerial Economics of the Institute of Management Sciences organized and held in Brussels in August of 1961. The purpose of this symposium was to bring together management scientists to present papers on the use of the management sciences in promoting the economic development of the newly emerging nations of the world. Each of the speakers at this symposium has contributed a chapter to this volume. In some cases the chapters are identical to those presented at the symposium. In other cases the authors have modified their presentations to make them more suitable for presentation in book form. For various reasons, two of the European and one of the American contributions included in this publication were not presented at the symposium.

This volume is directed to management scientists. It is hoped that it will serve to focus their interest in exploring further how various tools which have been developed for use in the more advanced economies can be applied to the newly emerging countries. It is also hoped that some of these papers will present enough background on some of the more significant environmental differences between the emerging and more advanced economies so that ill-advised applications of operations research and management science techniques will be avoided.

The division of editorial duties in connection with this publication was generally done on the basis that M. Verhulst handled the European contributions and N. N. Barish handled the American contributions. The editors thank the contributors to this volume for their wholehearted co-operation and for their devotion of the time and energy necessary to preparing and submitting their manuscripts. We are greatly indebted to Miss Justine L. Schmalzl, for assistance in the preparation of this volume.

NORMAN N. BARISH, *New York*
MICHEL VERHULST, *Paris*

PART ONE

PLANNING FOR DEVELOPMENT

1

A FRAMEWORK FOR PRODUCT-MARKET PLANNING*

J. FRED WESTON

University of California, Los Angeles

THE expressions "less developed" and "more fully developed" countries suggest degrees of development. W. W. Rostow has developed a concept of stages of development to provide a systematic theory of the economic growth of nations.† In his brilliant exposition of the theory, Professor Rostow has developed its implications for government foreign policy. Among the many other applications of the generalizations it occurred to me that the stages of development doctrine holds useful insights for entrepreneurial planning. It is the purpose of the present paper to suggest how the framework of stages of development provides useful guidelines for product-market planning for entrepreneurs in countries at any stage of development.

I. THE THEORY OF STAGES OF DEVELOPMENT

A brief recapitulation of Rostow's stages of growth theory is first required as essential background. Rostow identifies five stages of economic development:

* This study was facilitated by a Ford Foundation faculty summer research grant from the Division of Research, Graduate School of Business, UCLA. The assistance of Mr. Youngil Lim is gratefully acknowledged.

† W. W. Rostow, *The Stages of Economic Growth* (Cambridge University Press, England, 1961); *The Process of Economic Growth* (Oxford University Press, England, 1953).

Traditional Society
Transitional Society
Take-off
Technological Maturity
High Mass-consumption

Traditional Society

In the traditional society economic change and improvements are not sufficient to increase output *per capita*. A high proportion of resources are in agriculture. The social system is tied to family and clan holdings of land. Social mobility is limited; custom dominates; little economic exchange in organized markets takes place. The level of *per capita* product is low.

Transitional Society

In the general case, the transition is stimulated by contacts with outside cultures which break the hold of custom on the social structure, the political system, and production methods. The proximate economic manifestation of the change is an increase in the productivity of agriculture by the application of relatively simple equipment, improved methods or strategic supplements to soil chemicals.

The development of an agricultural surplus does three things. It frees additional labor for non-agricultural operations.* It provides a surplus for financing imports which further increase productivity. It develops an expanded supply of loanable funds for the modern sector. The agricultural surplus may also finance some of the required social overhead capital—transport, education, and power supply. The development of the social overhead capital is also likely to be supplied by foreign loans and grants and domestic government support.

* Disguised unemployment among persons in agriculture increases the elasticity of labor supply.

Take-off

The take-off is an acceleration in a nation's growth rate. Productive investment rises from 5 per cent or less of national product to over 10 per cent. One or more leading manufacturing sectors must emerge to provide momentum for overall growth. No one pattern is required for every take-off.

Historically, the leading sectors have ranged from cotton textiles, timber, pulp, dairy products, through heavy-industry complexes based on railroads and military end-products, and finally to a variety of consumers' goods. The productive improvements which detonate the burst of expansion in the leading sectors induce increased requirements and create external economics for other sectors. An enormous increase takes place in the capital stock. The society must generate sufficient capital for the key sectors and have a high rate of plough-back of profits to finance the supplementary growth sectors stimulated.

Illustrative take-off dates:*

Country	Take-off	Country	Take-off
Great Britain	1783–1802	Russia	1890–1914
France	1830–60	Canada	1896–1914
Belgium	1833–60	Argentina	1935–
United States	1843–60	Turkey	1937–
Germany	1850–73	India	1952–
Sweden	1868–90	China	1952–
Japan	1878–1900		

Technological Maturity

Technological maturity is the effective application of modern technology to the full range of a society's economic activity. New leading sectors gather momentum to replace the older leading sectors of the take-off. Capital formation rises to over 20 per cent of

* W. W. Rostow, *The Stages of Economic Growth*, p. 38.

national product. The range of industry is broadened from coal, iron and other producers' materials to supply a limited number of capital equipment goods to a wider range of industrial machinery, machine tools, chemicals and electrical and electronic products. The new leading sectors will be determined not only by the technologies available, but by the comparative resource advantages of different countries, endowed and developed.*

High Mass-consumption

One of the fruits of technological maturity is the rise of income *per capita* to levels which provide purchasing power beyond food, shelter and clothing necessities. This surplus income can be used in a number of ways. It can be used to purchase consumer durables such as autos or household appliances. The consumer durables industries would then emerge as the new leading sectors for sustaining growth in the economy. However, the income surplus can also be used to purchase increased military and political power, or to redistribute income and services through welfare state programs, or further to extend modern technology, or to increase population or to increase leisure. Choices between a number of economic and spiritual alternatives are both luxuries and penalties of the affluent society.

The foregoing is a brief outline of the broad patterns of economic change. Among the many uses to which the theory may be applied, the implications for entrepreneurial decision-making are here considered.

---

* Rostow suggests that the take-off averages some 20 years and the drive to maturity requires an additional 40 years. He provides "rough symbolic" dates for technological maturity:

Great Britain	1850	Sweden	1930
United States	1900	Japan	1940
Germany	1910	Russia	1950
France	1910	Canada	1950

II. GENERALITY OF THE CONCEPTS

The stages of economic development suggest a growth pattern for a nation's income *per capita* following the familiar S-shaped growth curve as shown in Fig. 1.

The parameters of this S-shaped curve, its position and slope, depend upon the behavior of the aggregate of industries in the nation's economy. This represents the aggregation of high-growth-rate industries, low-growth-rate industries, and declining industries.

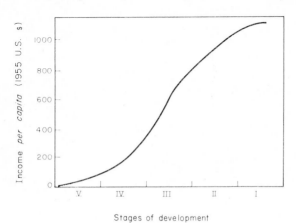

Stages of development

Fig. 1.   *Income* per capita *in relation to stage of development.*

Figure 2 shows growth patterns at the levels of product, industry, and firm. S-shaped growth curves are again illustrated. The similarity of the patterns would, of course, present a triviality without a theory explaining the pattern of the curves. For this brief presentation, suffice it to explain the portions of the curve below the inflection point and above the inflection point.

Below the inflection point, of course, the sales for a product are increasing at an increasing rate. The main explanation for this is that a reservoir of needs is being met so that substantial new layers of demands are being satisfied. In addition, the development of the new product in itself is probably likely to have favorable effects both

B

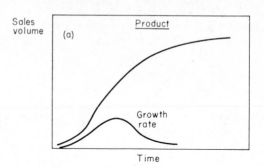

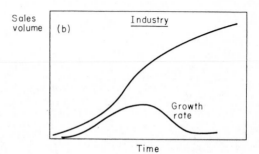

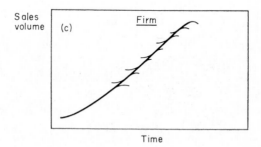

Fig. 2.

from income elasticity of demand and from price elasticity of demand reactions.

The inflection point is reached as the reservoir of demands has been substantially satisfied. Replacement demand or the basic growth factor upon which demand depends will take over. The volume of sales for the product begins to level off and perhaps even turn down. The essential mechanism for the slowing of growth and eventual turn down is the availability of the product substitutes. Since an industry is defined as a collection of firms producing a particular product, the picture of the life cycle of the industry and its growth pattern will parallel that indicated in Fig. 2(b).

However, the situation for the individual firm can be significantly different. The life cycle of volume for the firm in the first instance parallels that of the product of industry modified by some scalar reflecting the firm's share of the market. However, as the industry or product goes into a slower rate of growth the firm can be expected to diversify for the purpose of maintaining a satisfactory or a target growth rate. By effective diversification into more rapidly growing areas, the life cycle of the volume of sales for an individual firm can be represented by a number of S-curves superimposed on one another which gives a resultant curve similar in appearance to the S-shaped curve for the product of industry but more elongated and with substantially different parameters.

As the firm introduces new products there is a possibility of a moderate dip. As new products take hold there is likely to be a more vigorous rate of growth, at least temporarily. If a firm is a multi-product firm, the declines and fast rises may cancel out so that the resulting growth rate for the firm may be relatively constant. The resultant rate may reflect either the possibilities of the firm's basic technological or marketing skills or the target rate that the firm has set for itself.

But, of course, the product diversification or other product market strategies which result in an elongation of the life cycle of the growth of sales and the very existence of an individual firm do not come about automatically. This is the result of effective planning by the firm. The goal of this effective planning is for the firm to make the best adjustment to its environment or to identify the nature of its present and prospective environment as effectively as possible. The firm then adopts those policies which represent the most effective adaptation to that environment; or the firm carries out its behavior in such a way that, given the environment in which it operates, the firm has the greatest likelihood of being adopted by that environment. Alternatively, the firm continuously seeks new environments in which more favorable opportunities will be found, given its basic technological and marketing skills. Finally, the firm seeks to develop new skills and capabilities and experience which will enable it to achieve more effective performance in the evolving environments.

The development of an effective product-market strategy for achieving the favorable growth performance for the individual firm takes many things into account. Among these the stages of development concept provides a useful framework. We therefore return to the stages of development concept, clothing it now more concretely.

III. BEHAVIOR OF BASIC ECONOMIC MAGNITUDES IN SUCCESSIVE STAGES OF DEVELOPMENT

An initial exemplification of the stages of development hypothesis is contained in the material in Table 1.

On the basis of selected data the countries of the world are grouped in Rostow's framework of the five stages of growth. The table contains data for eight economic variables:

These are all significant variables for indicating the degree of maturity of a total economy. However, three are of greatest importance. They are *per capita* income, the percentage of fixed capital formation to gross national product, and the percentage of population in agriculture. These were the three primary criteria for deciding upon the ranking of countries by stages of development. The manner in which these criteria were used to rank countries is set forth in Table 2.

TABLE 1. *Stages of Economic Development*

	1*	2	3	4	5	6	7	8	9
GROUP I									
United States	2343	387·2	3	17	8·3	106·2	12	19·1	13·8
Canada	1667	26·0	4	24	7·6	4·1	19	5·3	6·3
Switzerland	1229	6·1	4	22	2·9	0·2	17	1·31	1·77
Sweden	1165	8·5	4	20	4·2	2·1	20	1·94	2·21
Iceland	1146	0·18	NA	31	2·9			0·06	0·09
France	1046	45·2	4	17	2·4	15·8	36	4·5	5·6
Belgium	1015	9·3	3	16	4·1	5·9	12	3·2	3·3
Luxembourg	1015	9·3	2	22		3·2	26	NA	NA
United Kingdom	998	51·1	4·5	15	4·9	20·1	6	9·3	10·9
Norway	969	3·3	3	29	5·3	0·2	26	0·77	1·21
Finland	941	4·0	4	25	1·9	0·2	46	0·77	0·88
Denmark	913	4·0	2	17	4·1	5·9	12	1·11	1·31
West Germany	762	38·1	8	22	3·4	21·3	23	7·4	6·6
Netherlands	708	7·6	6	23	2·2	1·0	19	2·9	3·7
GROUP II									
New Zealand	1249	2·7	3	24	2·8		18	0·77	0·75
Australia	1215	10·9	NA	27	3·7	2·2	15	1·90	1·94
Israel	540	0·94	14	22	1·1			0·11	0·36
Austria	532	3·7	6	24	2·2	1·8	32	0·85	0·97
Ireland	509	1·5	2	14	1·4		40	0·30	0·51
Argentina	460	8·8	1	18	0·9	0·2	25	0·94	1·13
Italy	442	21·2	5	20	1·1	5·4	40	2·16	3·17
Japan	240	21·3	8	21	1·0	9·4	45	2·50	3·23
Mexico	187	5·6	6	14	0·7	0·5	58	0·69	1·07
GROUP III									
Venezuela	762	4·4	NA	27	2·0		41	2·12	1·25
Uruguay	569	1·5	NA		0·8			0·04	0·03
Puerto Rico	526	1·2	NA	14	0·8		39	0·37	0·58
Union of South Africa	381	5·2	NA	24	2·3	1·6	53	1·18	1·52
Chile	360	2·5	3·5	8	1·0	0·3	30	0·54	0·35

* Column headings:
1. Income *per capita* in dollars.
2. Total GNP in $ billions.
3. Annual growth rate in *per capita* income.
4. Fixed capital formation as a percentage of GNP
5. Power consumption in tons *per capita* of energy equivalent of metric tons of coal.
6. Crude steel production in million metric tons.
7. Percentage of the labor force in agriculture.
8. Exports in $ billions.
9. Imports in $ billions.

TABLE 1 (*contd.*)

	1*	2	3	4	5	6	7	8	9
Columbia	330	4·2	5	12	0·5	0·1		0·60	0·66
Brazil	262	15·3	6	15	0·4	1·2	61	1·48	1·23
Greece	239	2·0	6	14	0·3		48	0·19	0·46
Philippines	201	4·4	NA	7	0·2		66	0·44	0·60
Portugal	201	1·8	3	13	0·4		48	0·30	0·44
Rhodesia	134	0·95	8	34	0·6		12	0·51	0·50
GROUP IV									
Cuba	361	2·2	NA		0·6		42	0·67	0·71
Panama	350	0·32	NA	11	0·4		51	0·03	0·10
Costa Rica	307	0·29	NA	16	0·3		68	0·07	0·09
Malaya	298	2·2	NA	10	0·4		65	1·36	1·36
Turkey	276	6·5	5	15	0·3	0·2		0·30	0·41
Lebanon	269	0·38	3		0·5			0·04	0·24
Spain	254	7·4	NA		0·8	1·2	49	0·44	0·77
Nicaragua	254	0·32	NA		0·1		68	0·06	0·07
El Salvador	244	0·53	NA		0·1		63	0·11	0·10
Dominican Republic	205	0·49	NA	22	0·2			0·12	0·13
Ecuador	204	0·75	NA	16			49	0·12	0·10
Iraq	195	0·96	NA			0·3		0·48	0·32
Jamaica	180	0·29	NA	13				0·11	0·16
Guatemala	179	0·58	5	15	0·2			0·11	0·14
Morocco	159	1·5	NA		0·2			0·34	0·44
Paraguay	140	0·22	NA				55	0·04	0·03
Peru	140	1·3	NA	21	0·3			0·31	0·36
Ghana	135	0·62	NA	14	0·1			0·24	0·24
Egypt	135	3·1	NA		0·2		51	0·41	0·53
Tunisia	131	0·49	NA		0·2			0·11	0·19
Indonesia	128	10·5	NA	5	0·1			0·88	0·86
Ceylon	122	1·05	NA	12	0·1		53	0·36	0·34
Syria	111	0·45	NA		0·2			0·16	0·19
Liberia	103	0·16	NA					NA	NA
Taiwan	102	1·6	NA					0·12	0·19
Iran	100	2·1	NA					0·25	0·30
India	72	27·4	3·5		0·1	1·7	71	1·3	1·7
Pakistan	56	4·6	NA		0·1		77	0·34	0·36
GROUP V									
Saudi Arabia	166	1·2	NA					0·84	0·27
Honduras	137	0·23	NA	15	0·2		83	0·07	0·07

For key to column headings see p. 9.

TABLE 1 (*cont.*)

	1*	2	3	4	5	6	7	8	9
Vietnam	133	1·6	NA					0·04	0·22
Thailand	100	2·0	3				85	0·33	0·36
Sudan	100	0·89	NA		0·1			0·19	0·13
Jordan	96	0·14	NA		0·1			0·01	0·06
Libya	90	0·10	NA					NA	NA
Korea	80	1·8	0·8	9	0·2			0·02	0·34
Haiti	75	0·26	NA				83	0·04	0·05
Bolivia	66	0·21	NA		0·2		64	0·08	0·10
Ethiopia	54	0·86	NA					0·07	0·07
Burma	52	1·0	7·8	19				0·24	0·20
Laos		NA	NA					0·00	0·04
Cambodia		NA	NA					0·04	0·06

Source: Based on data in *Facts and Figures*, a handbook prepared for use at the International Industrial Development Conference, San Francisco, California, October 1957, sponsored by Time-Life International and the Stanford Research Institute.

TABLE 2. *Criteria for Grouping Countries by Stage of Growth*

	V	IV	III	II	I
A. *Per capita* income	Less than $200	$200–400	$400–600	$600–800	Greater than $800
B. Per cent capital formation to GNP	0–5	5–10	25–30	15–25	10–15
C. Per cent of population in agriculture	Greater than 80	60–80	40–60	20–40	0–20

Per capita income was given greatest weight, but with qualifications made from judging other relevant factors. If capital formation represents a large percentage of GNP, the rank of the country was promoted one level higher, although the *per capita* income was low. If the percentage of the population engaged in agriculture is very large, 70 per cent or more, although *per capita* income may be higher than a given rank, one level of rank is lowered. When the amount of production of steel is very large as compared with the percentage of people engaged in agriculture, the rank is raised. The least important factor for deciding rank was the amount of power consumed in terms of tons of coal because this may change according to the temperature zone in which the country is located.

From the data in Table 1 a number of generalizations can be drawn. Figure 3 shows an interesting reversal pattern. Income *per capita* grows as we move from stage V to stage I in the familiar S-shaped pattern.

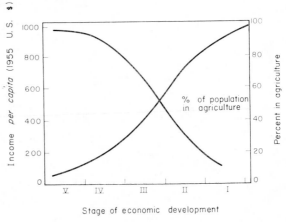

Fig. 3.

However, the percentage of the population in agriculture represents almost the complement to the level of income *per capita*.

Certain interesting relationships expressed in terms of growth rates are set forth in Fig. 4.

The growth rate in total gross national product or in income *per capita* is shown first. This curve will be the first derivative of the total curve. Fixed capital formation as a percentage of GNP will parallel the growth-rate curve. However, its relationship to *per capita* income is somewhat different, depending primarily upon the capital output ratio. For example, suppose GNP grows at a 3 per cent rate, population grows at a 1 per cent rate with a capital output ratio of 3.

For *per capita* income to grow at 2 per cent per annum, the ratio of fixed capital formation to GNP would have to be 9 per cent. If under these circumstances a *per capita* income growth of 3 per cent were sought, GNP would have to grow at 4 per cent, and with a capital output ratio of 3 the ratio of fixed capital formation to GNP would have to rise to 12 per cent. If GNP is to grow at 8 per cent the ratio of fixed capital formation to GNP would have to be 24 per cent. Thus this ratio is a function of the growth rate in GNP rather than the total amount of GNP itself.

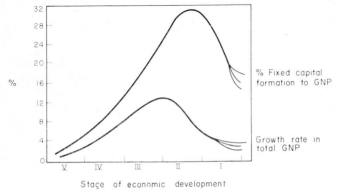

FIG. 4.

Another significant relationship suggested by the pattern of behavior of income *per capita* is the distribution of individual incomes. The nature of this distribution is suggested in Fig. 5.

During the first stage the average level of income is relatively low, with substantial inequality. In the transitional stage the entrepreneurs responsible for improving productivity will reap very large gains with only negligible gains for the lower income groups. As a consequence, the average level of income is increased only slightly while the inequality in income distribution is further aggravated.

In the stage of the take-off a great increase in marketplace economic activity occurs so that the average level of income is increased substantially. The income of the lower income groups is improved so that while the degree of income inequality is not changed greatly the curve is shifted upward.

In the stage of technological maturity many of the gains due to increased productivity of the capital stock are transmitted to workers in the form of higher wages. As a consequence the income distribution is still shifted upward and the slope of the curve now begins to be reduced. Finally, in the fifth stage, the curve is tipped over

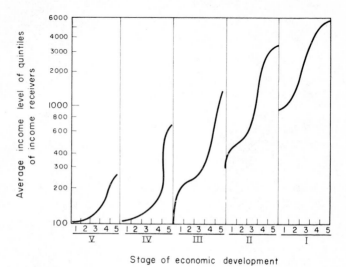

Stage of economic development

FIG. 5.   *Income distribution by stage of economic development.*

substantially so that the number of persons with incomes of $5000 a year or more becomes substantially larger.

The above basic patterns follow directly from the concept of the stages of economic development for different countries. However, in this particular analysis we are not interested in these relationships simply for understanding the behavior and operation of individual economies. Rather we seek to apply this material for improving entrepreneurial product-market planning. How this may be done is taken up in the following section.

IV. PATTERNS OF GROWTH OF MAJOR SECTORS IN RELATIONSHIP TO A COUNTRY'S STAGE OF DEVELOPMENT

The significance for business planning of the foregoing is suggested by analysis initiated by Chenery. Certain basic relationships are suggested by his data summarized in Fig. 6.

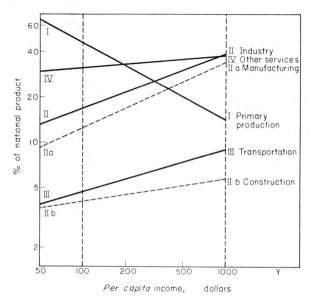

FIG. 6.   *The share of major sectors in national product.*
(Logarithmic Scale. Population 10 million.)

Source: Hollis B. Chenery, "Patterns of Industrial Growth",
American Economic Review, **50** (September 1960), 636.

Figure 6 shows the share of major sectors in national product at different stages of a nation's economic development. Primary production is seen to decline from over 60 per cent to 16 per cent. Industry, in contrast, rises from 15 per cent in group V countries to 38 per cent in group I countries. The detail of these patterns of the relative share of major sectors of national product is presented for the individual countries as well as by groups in Table 3.

However, even more significant from the standpoint of business planning is the growth rate by different sectors or selected industries at different time periods and at different stages of the country's economic development. Data relevant to this matter are set forth in Table 4, taken from a recent study entitled *Patterns on Industrial Growth*, by the Department of Economic and Social Affairs of the United Nations. Here, however, the groupings are in terms of only four classes rather than five.

Certain distinctive differences are immediately noted. For the class IV countries very high growth rates are observed in metal products and basic metals during the last 5-year period. In contrast the growth rate for these products in the class I industries is either very small or negative. The growth rates in products involving a greater degree of fabrication are relatively low at the class IV stage, become quite high in the class II stage, and then decline to lower levels in the class I stage.

However, the difficulty with these compilations of data is that the groupings of the products are too broad and not sufficiently analytical to provide a key to real understanding for business planning. However, the data are suggestive and provide a basis for a more analytical statement of relative growth rates which is the focus of this presentation.

The degree of generalization now set out is extreme to the point of pushing theoretical relationships too far. The deficiencies in the validity of the concepts are offset by the useful organizing framework provided for product-market entrepreneurial planning.

Table 5 seeks to bring together some of the key variables for countries in different stages in economic development. The leading characteristics of countries at the different categories or stages are related to relative factor prices and product specialization both with regard to manufacture import and export.

TABLE 3. *GNP Composition of Selected Countries by* per capita *Income Groups*

Average share of major sectors in GNP, 1950–55

Country	Per capita income	IA Agriculture	IB Mining	I Total primary (IA&IB)	II Transportation	III Industry	IV Services
GROUP V Less than $100							
Burma	50	43·9	1·4	45·3	1·7	14·2	38·8
Bolivia	55	28·9	25·4	54·3	—	19·8	—
India	58	48·4	0·9	49·3	—	16·6	—
Kenya	66	49·0	0·9	49·9	7·0	13·5	29·6
Pakistan	68	58·8	0·2	59·0	2·8	11·2	27·0
Belgian Congo	70	27·0	21·4	48·4	8·3	17·5	25·8
South Korea	74	42·3	1·2	43·5	1·9	14·7	39·9
Thailand	80	49·1	1·7	50·8	4·2	14·9	30·1
Average	65	43·4	6·6	50·0	4·3	15·3	31·9
GROUP IV $100–$200							
Egypt	112	38·9	2·1	41·0	5·0	19·4	34·6
Ceylon	117	53·4	0·1	53·5	7·4	13·3	25·8
Rhodesia and Nyasaland	118	18·8	32·3	51·1	—	15·8	—
Iraq	126	23·9	26·4	50·3	—	19·3	—
Peru	137	32·7	11·9	44·6	—	19·9	—
Honduras	143	52·3	1·6	53·9	5·0	14·0	34·6
El Salvador	147	52·4	0·5	52·9	—	—	—
Ecuador	150	38·9	2·1	41·0	5·0	19·4	34·6
Philippines	150	42·7	1·4	44·1	2·9	14·8	38·2
Nicaragua	155	40·5	0·5	41·0	—	—	—
Turkey	156	45·0	1·4	46·4	7·1	16·8	29·7
Dominican Republic	160	42·5	0·5	43·0	—	18·2	—
Guatemala	164	45·5	0·4	45·9	—	21·2	—
Japan	181	23·4	3·0	26·4	7·0	29·7	43·9
Brazil	184	27·6	0·6	28·2	10·8	23·3	37·7
Average	147	38·6	5·7	44·3	6·3	18·9	34·9

TABLE 3 (*contd.*)

Country	Per capita income	IA	IB	I	II	III	IV
GROUP III $200–$300							
Portugal	200	29·1	0·8	29·9	4·8	36·9	28·4
Greece	220	35·2	1·1	36·3	6·5	24·2	33·0
Mexico	229	20·2	4·1	24·3	4·2	23·3	48·2
Colombia	242	39·0	2·6	41·6	6·4	16·8	35·2
Italy	250	25·1	1·2	26·3	6·3	39·6	27·8
Union of South Africa	280	15·4	12·5	27·9	8·2	25·9	38·0
Chile	285	14·9	5·4	20·3	7·3	20·6	51·8
Costa Rica	287	44·3	0·1	44·4	—	15·0	—
Average	249	27·9	3·5	31·4	6·2	25·3	37·5
GROUP II $300–$600							
Lebanon	327	19·7	0·1	19·8	4·6	16·0	59·6
Austria	370	15·3	3·0	18·3	5·1	50·1	26·5
Ireland	423	32·5	1·0	33·5	—	25·1	—
Netherlands	448	12·0	1·0	13·0	8·5	41·9	36·6
Venezuela	540	8·0	27·0	35·0	—	24·2	—
Argentina	542	18·1	1·1	19·2	—	28·7	—
West Germany	563	9·9	3·0	12·9	7·7	47·1	32·3
Israel	565	12·2	0·6	12·8	7·7	28·5	51·0
Average	472	16·0	4·6	20·6	6·7	32·7	41·2
GROUP I $600 and over							
Finland	727	24·7	0·2	24·9	7·2	41·1	26·8
Norway	732	14·3	1·6	15·9	17·0	36·3	30·8
France	740	16·0	1·8	17·8	9·0	31·2	42·0
United Kingdom	757	5·2	3·5	8·7	8·4	44·9	38·0
Denmark	762	20·5	0·2	20·7	9·0	36·5	33·8
Belgium	824	8·4	4·9	13·3	9·0	45·8	31·9
Sweden	943	8·0	2·0	10·0	7·0	48·0	35·0
New Zealand	958	23·7	0·9	24·6	8·9	29·9	36·6
Australia	972	18·3	2·7	21·0	—	36·4	—
United States	1065	5·5	1·7	7·2	6·1	34·7	52·0
Canada	1291	12·1	3·9	16·0	7·6	38·5	37·9
Average	888	14·2	2·1	16·3	8·9	38·5	36·5

TABLE 3 (*contd.*)

Country	Per capita income	IA	IB	I	II	III	IV
SUMMARY							
Group V	65	43·4	6·6	50·0	4·3	15·3	31·9
Group IV	147	38·6	5·7	44·3	6·3	18·9	34·9
Group III	249	27·9	3·5	31·4	6·2	25·3	37·5
Group II	472	16·0	4·6	20·6	6·7	32·7	41·2
Group I	888	14·2	2·1	16·3	8·9	38·5	36·5

Source: H. B. Chenery, "Patterns of Industrial Growth", *The American Economic Review*, September 1960, p. 632.

While the material in Table 5 is useful for indicating general relationships, the situation with individual countries in any of the countries would doubtless be influenced by the following. Most important is the natural resource pattern with which the country is originally endowed or that it has historically developed. A second important factor is the strength and pervasiveness of the social values of the traditional society, some of which may persist after the country has emerged from this stage. Of great importance is the relative role of government policy—its direction, the distribution of power in the country, and how this power is exercised.

Another important human factor is the kinds of education, the degree of public education provided, and the number of years during which public education has been provided to the population. A number of these foregoing factors will influence both social and geographic mobility which, in turn, will have important economic influences. Another factor of great importance influencing the pattern of a nation's development is its location in relationship to trade patterns with other nations. In addition, the existence of pre-datory forces will stimulate both military and non-military reactions on the part of both government and private business groups.

With these qualifications in mind the material in Table 5 is useful for setting into a broad framework the dynamics of world economic

TABLE 4. *Average Annual Rate of Change in Output for Selected Periods, Manufacturing—Selected Industries*

Area or class of industrialization and period	Food, bev., tobac.	Tex-tiles	Cloth., foot-wear, etc.	Wood prod. and furn.	Paper and paper prod.	Chem. and related prod.	Non-metallic min. prod.	Basic metals	Metal prod.
World									
1938–58	3·1	2·3	1·6	2·9	4·5	6·7	4·8	4·4	6·3
1938–48	2·6	2·2	1·0	3·2	3·3	5·5	4·0	5·1	6·3
1948–53	3·9	3·2	2·9	3·0	6·3	8·9	6·6	6·3	9·6
1953–58	3·2	1·6	1·7	2·3	5·2	6·8	4·6	1·2	2·9
Class I*									
1938–58	2·9	1·8	1·5	2·7	4·5	6·6	4·4	4·2	6·4
1938–48	2·8	2·0	1·0	3·2	3·7	6·5	4·3	6·1	7·0
1948–53	3·4	3·2	2·7	3·2	5·9	8·0	5·7	5·4	9·6
1953–58	2·5	0·0	1·2	1·2	4·6	5·6	3·2	−0·6	−1·9
Class II*									
1938–58	3·4	1·6	2·1	3·1	4·0	6·8	4·6	6·9	4·9
1938–48	1·0	1·8	1·0	3·2	−0·7	2·1	1·6	2·4	2·4
1948–53	7·3	1·7	3·6	4·2	8·3	13·1	7·3	11·7	7·6
1953–58	4·1	1·2	2·7	1·7	9·2	10·0	7·6	11·1	7·1
Class III*									
1938–58	4·3	3·3	3·4	4·0	5·5	6·2	5·9	4·9	7·2
1938–48	1·3	−1·0	2·4	3·9	−1·8	−3·1	1·0	−1·7	−2·1
1948–53	7·4	8·2	3·4	1·0	15·1	18·3	11·1	12·0	16·4
1953–58	7·3	7·1	5·4	7·3	10·5	12·6	10·4	10·9	16·4
Class IV*									
1938–58	3·5	2·1	NA	NA	8·3	5·4	8·2	5·8	8·4
1938–48	2·2	0·4	NA	NA	2·7	3·9	5·5	3·5	5·8
1948–53	4·4	0·2	NA	NA	15·3	6·2	12·2	8·9	7·7
1953–58	5·1	5·4	NA	NA	12·4	7·7	9·4	7·1	14·2

* Classes of degree of industrialization.

Countries were grouped into four classes according to degree of industrialization, in terms of estimated value added, in current U.S. dollars, during 1953 in manufacturing per head of population. The intervals in U.S. dollars for each class were as follows:

Class   I—$200 and over   Class III—$50–99
Class II—$100–199   Class IV—under $50

This criterion therefore reflected the extent to which the population was employed in manufacturing as well as the productivity of the labor so engaged.

Source: Patterns of Industrial Growth, 1938–1958 (U.N., Department of Economic and Social Affairs, New York, 1960), pp. 76–9, 437.

TABLE 5. *Stages of Economic Development*

Stages	Relative factor prices			Product specialization	
	Workers	Land	Capital	Import	Export
Five categories: I. Mass-consumption (a) Mass-consumption of consumers' goods and services central force in economic and social life. (b) Urban and white collar jobs larger proportion.	Dear	Mod.	Cheap	Raw materials. Consumer durable and non-durables	Advanced equipment
(c) Increased resources to social welfare and security. (d) U.S., U.K., Canada, France, W. Germany.				Standard equipment	Some mass-production items
II. Technological maturity (a) 40 years after end of take-off. (b) New industries for old: from coal, iron and heavy engineering to machine tools, chemicals, electrical equipment.	Mod.	Cheap	Mod.	Raw materials. Industrial machinery	Less of industrial materials
(c) Rearrangement of imports and exports; more raw materials imported and more manufactured goods exported. U.S.S.R., Mexico and Argentina entering; Japan now.					Components of equipment. Some consumer non-durables

C

Stages	Relative factor prices			Product specialization	
	Workers	Land	Capital	Import	Export
III. Take-off (a) Technological devt. or transportation. (b) Investment rises to 10 per cent of national income from 5 per cent. (c) Diversion of manpower into industries; agriculture and trade must support the population. (d) England 1783–1800; France and United States 1830–60; Germany 1850–75; Japan 1875–1900; China post-1950; Brazil and Venezuela; U.S.S.R. in 1920's.	Cheap	Mod.	Mod.	Machine produce. Industrial materials. Some equipment for fabrication	Same as II plus industrial materials
IV. Transitional society: devt. of three preconditions for growth (a) Agricultural surplus. (b) Traded for imports. (c) Devt. of social overhead capital: transport, education, sources of power. India, Pakistan, Egypt, Iraq, Indonesia.	Cheap	Mod.	Dear	Social overhead capital. Simple agricultural tools	Tropics. Raw materials. Minerals
V. Traditional society: custom and slow growth	Cheap	Dear	Dear	—	—

development, including its implications for businessmen and decision-makers at all levels.

We start with the traditional society dominated by custom and slow growth. Relative factor prices are as follows. Labor is cheap, land is dear, and capital is dear, all relatively. Obviously, capital instruments are the most scarce resources. Land is also scarce, as evidenced by the fact that a large number of people are seeking more land than can be obtained. From the principles of relative scarcities it is clear that labor is overabundant in relation to land and capital. Nothing is shown in the column for product specialization, imports and exports, because traditional society is virtually closed off from the world of international commerce.

When the preconditions for growth have been established, the country moves into a transitional society. With the application of simple capital instruments to the land or the use of fertilizer, land becomes relatively less scarce compared to the other factors of production, so land may be considered to be only moderately expensive rather than dear. At this stage the transitional country begins to develop effectively its indigenous agricultural and basic raw materials. Thus, they will increase exports of tropical fruits and products, raw materials, and minerals. They import simple agricultural tools and social overhead capital, including an import of financial aid to provide for the social overhead capital.

Once the social overhead capital or the infrastructure has been developed, the country has arrived at the take-off stage. Up to this point the economy has been primarily agricultural.

At the take-off the beginnings of a commercial, financial, and industrial side of economic life develop. Investment becomes a substantial percentage of national product. An increasing diversion of manpower from agriculture into industry takes place. With the increase in the pace of development, capital becomes less scarce and may be regarded as having become only moderately expensive, along with land. Labor is still relatively cheap.

Exports can now be augmented by industrial materials that require only a moderate degree of fabrication. Imports continue the pattern of further developing the infrastructure. In addition, there are imports of relatively simple machines for the production of industrial materials and some equipment for a moderate degree of fabrication of parts of machinery and fabricated metals.

As the country arrives at a stage of technological maturity the continued development of the capital stock leads to a substitution of new industries for old. The coal, iron, and heavy basic industries move to a more complex type of industrial composition including machine tools, chemicals, and electrical and electronic equipment.

The country begins to export less of industrial materials and more consumer non-durables and durables. The country now begins to fabricate components of equipment. They are not producers of complete systems, but they are the products of components or sub-systems. The country now begins to import relatively more raw materials because their relative advantage is now in the areas of more fabrication rather than less fabrication. They continue to import industrial machinery in order to round out their technological capabilities.

Capital goes from moderate to cheap. Land at this stage is likely to be cheap relative to capital. This is the stage at which the construction of buildings tends to be spread out horizontally. Workers have become moderately expensive, as evidenced by the beginning of increased substitution of machinery for labor.

As we move to the stage of mass consumption, capital now becomes relatively the cheapest. This is the period of the high rise buildings. There is considerable substitution of capital for labor because labor has now become relatively dear.

At this stage of its development, a country actually becomes a raw material importer to a greater extent because the land is less expensive in less developed countries and hence raw materials can be produced more cheaply there. The country is likely to import consumer durables and non-durables to a higher degree because of the high percentage of spending allocated in these directions. This is reinforced by the ability of other countries increasingly to produce these items, especially as they achieve mass-production operations. The nation develops sufficient surplus income to have a number of alternatives in the allocation of resources.

With the broad patterns developed in Table 5, taking into account relative factor prices and varying kinds of product specialization at each stage, the framework can be developed even more concretely. This is suggested by Table 6.

Table 6 sets out the per annum growth rates of production of selected economic sectors as a function of the nation's stage of economic development. In addition to the growth rates, the logic of growth for each sector in a stage I economy has a function of certain key economic variables is also set out. The phasing of the growth rates of different sectors is based on production. Production will be the net resultant of domestic consumption adjusted by imports and exports. The import–export patterns outlined in connection with Table 5 are taken into account in setting forth the production growth rates for the sectors in Table 6. These will reflect the import and export patterns suggested by the division of labor specified in relationship to the stage of the country's economic development.

Brief comments will now be made on each of the sectors.

1. Consumer non-durable goods have relatively slow growth in stages V and IV. A beginning of growth emerges in stage III. The greatest growth rates occur in stage II because of the expansion of consumer incomes. However, by stage I the basic needs of the population have been met and the growth in consumer non-durable goods sectors settles down to some function of the population growth rate. This can be modified only by product innovations which will make consumption a function of income or a change in spending patterns.

2. For consumer durable goods the pattern is the same for old and new through stage II. The growth rate is virtually nil until stage II, when there is a tremendous burst, whether the country goes into a stage of mass-consumption goods or not. For established consumer durable goods in stage I, the growth rate is a function of replacement demand. However, for new items the growth rate is a function of the growth rate of the higher income groups generally.

3. A distinction must be made for growth rates of producer materials. For raw materials the greatest rate comes in stage III. For semi-fabricated materials the greatest rate comes in stage II. For fabricated materials the greatest growth rate also comes in stage

TABLE 6. *Per Annum Growth Rates of Production of Selected Economic Sectors as a Function of the Nation's Stage of Economic Development*

Economic sector	Stage of development					Growth in stage I, a function of
	V	IV	III	II	I	
1. Consumer non-durable goods	0	0	2	4–5	2	Population growth rate
2. Consumer durable goods:						
(a) Old	0	0	0·5	15–20	2–4	Replacement demand
(b) New	0	0	0·5	15–20	8–12	Growth rate of over $10,000 income group
3. Producer materials:						
(a) Raw	0	5–6	8–10	4–6	(1)–1	Growth rate of GNP; imports, exports
(b) Semi-fabricated	0	0–1	5–6	6–8	0–2	Growth rate of GNP; imports, exports
(c) Fabricated	0	0	1–2	8–10	2–4	Growth rate of GNP; imports, exports
4. Producer durables:						
(a) Parts	0	0–1	10–12	6–8	4–6	Change in growth rate of GNP
(b) Systems	0	0	2–3	16–18	6–8	Change in growth rate of GNP; sector, composition
5. Chemicals, electronics	0	0	1–2	6–8	10–14	Innovation rate
6. Agriculture	1–2	8–10	6–8	2–4	(4)–(2)	Population less imports
7. Extractive	1–2	8–12	18–22	6–8	1–2	GNP level less imports
8. Trade	0	6–8	20–24	10–12	4	Level of GNP
9. Finance	0	2–4	8–10	10–12	6–7	Shift to consumer durables and asset exchanges
10. Transportation	0	30–35	20–25	8–10	4	Level of GNP
11. Utilities	0	25–30	10–15	8–10	4	Growth of GNP; sector composition and relative growth
12. Services	0	1–2	3–4	4–5	7–9	Upward shift in income distribution
13. Government—non-military	0	6–8	5–6	2–3	5–7	Change in GNP
14. Government—military	0	1–2	2–4	16–20	3–4	Change in GNP

II, but persists at a higher level in stage I. The growth rate in stage I of the producer materials is a function of the growth rate of GNP modified by import and export patterns.

4. The production of producer's durable parts begins at a relatively high level in stage III and then begins to taper off. The greatest growth rate in complete producer's durables occurs in stage II as the country achieves technological maturity. However, a temporary glut in capital goods exists at this point and unless new expanding industries develop in stage I, the producer's durable goods industries will have negative growth rates in stage I. The growth rates indicated for stage I are based on a favorable growth rate in gross national product. This in turn presumes the continuing emergence of new growth sectors and a shift in sector composition which requires the use of capital goods to provide the basic industrial foundation for those activities.

5. Chemicals and electronics are taken as the prototypes of the advanced technology industries. They have virtually no growth until stage III, when the country has sufficient technological know-how to begin to develop competences in these areas. When stage I is reached, it can be expected that this is the high-growth area and the growth rate, of course, depends upon the effectiveness of innovation activities in the economy.

6. The agricultural sector reaches its greatest growth rate in the transitional stage. From that point on its relative importance diminishes. In fact, by stage I the annual growth rate of production in agriculture will be tied to the population growth rate less imports. Based on population growth rates alone, the growth rate in agriculture would be 1 to 2 per cent. But given the relative advantage in the world's division of labor as between stage V countries and stage I countries, the growth rate of agriculture in stage I countries is likely to represent a negative growth rate.

7. The extractive industries reach their peak in stage III. From that point onward the growth rates likewise begin to level off. In stage I the growth rate of the extractive industries is a function of gross national product levels less imports of metals and minerals.

8. Trade also in the take-off stage reaches its peak. The early manufacturing specialization of a country depends upon trade to provide the ingredients for further progress. At stage I the growth rate of trade becomes a function of the level of gross national product.

9. The growth pattern of finance parallels that of trade. In stage I the shift to consumer durables and their financing and increased activity in asset exchange makes for a greater growth rate in finance than the growth rate in GNP.

10, 11. Transportation and utilities grow at extremely high rates in stages IV and III in association with the development of the social infrastructure and to provide the means for further economic development. By stage I they have settled down to growth rates that are a function of the level of gross national product, sector composition and relative growth in sectors. Transportation and utilities often will have a renewed burst of activity as new leading growth sectors in the economy emerge.

12. In this discussion of services we are dealing with the kinds of services utilized in advanced economics. The growth rate of such services is a function of upward shifts in income distribution. Thus the growth rate of services would parallel the upward shift in the curve of income distribution set forth in Fig. 2.

13. Government non-military expenditures represent a wide range of government services. This profile suggests that government is likely to be most active in the transitional stage and still relatively high in the take-off. By the time technological maturity is reached, the need of government for directing economic growth or for providing social welfare services has greatly diminished because of the vigor of general growth of the economy as a whole. However, in addition, government military expenditures are likely to receive a larger share of the government revenue pie at stage II.

14. Government military expenditures show relatively moderate growth rates until stage II. In stage II the economy begins to develop a surplus which may express itself in new-found strength and political forcefulness in the international sphere. Thus government military

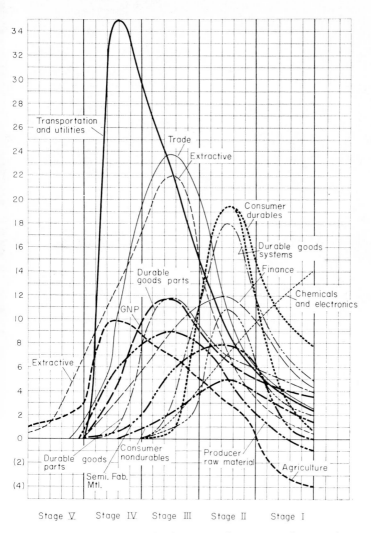

FIG. 7. *Time phasing of industry growth rates at each stage of economic development.*

expenditures are likely to take a much higher segment of government revenues during stage II. If the nation enters into the society of nations in stage I the growth rate in government military expenditures will decline sharply. However, in a world of international tension the growth rate in government military expenditures is likely to just about parallel, or be slightly below the growth rate in gross national product over the long run.

These generalizations on differential growth rates show an important difference in the time phasing of growth patterns as set forth in Fig. 7.

The material clearly has significant implications for entrepreneurial product-market planning.

V. IMPLICATIONS OF THE FRAMEWORK FOR BUSINESS DECISIONS

In business planning the scientist will typically lead the firm into an area 10 to 20 years too soon. The businessman left on his own is likely to arrive in the area 5 to 10 years too late. In the non-military business sector the scientist will lead the firm into areas that are technically feasible before practical bottlenecks and customer needs and acceptance have been fully developed. Most businessmen operate on an imitative basis, as described by Schumpeter in his theory of economic development. Effective business decision making, therefore, can usually draw on this framework which illustrates the time phasing of growth and development at different stages.

A few of the illustrative generalizations will indicate the way in which the framework can be used. For example, the capital goods industries are likely to be in a temporary glut at the end of stage II. Whether they will have a revival or not depends upon the relative growth rate in countries at emerging stages of development and whether new sectors—mass-consumption industries, the new technologies, government programs either for social welfare or for military purposes—require machinery for developing output capabilities in new industrial sectors. This framework provides perspective for business leaders in capital goods industries to obtain an understanding of the directions in which the pattern of their future sales is likely to go.

Stage IV industries are not yet likely to be ready to develop an industrial machinery or machine tool industry. For either individual businessmen or government to attempt to develop industries for producing producers' durable goods at this stage is likely to involve social costs from the standpoint of government and individual bankruptcy from the standpoint of the business firm. On the other hand, businesses in stage IV are likely to find fertile opportunities and attractive profit-making possibilities in areas such as food processing, cement, steel, and certain basic chemicals and drugs.

Countries that have reached stage I in economic development are not likely to provide attractive growth opportunities for business in agriculture, textiles, and mass-produced, simple type consumer durables. The country's relative advantage is likely to be in advanced complex machinery and in innovating of industrial systems in the areas of greatest technological fertility. For individual businessmen to go into the low-growth-rate areas is to invite unfavorable growth-to-capacity relationships in the industry and to result in low profit rates. Because of these unfavorable environments businessmen may seek government support to maintain such industries in the face of relative disadvantage in the world division of labor. Acquiescence on the part of governments in support of such industries results in the maintaining of sick industries. The country thereby is twisting its use of economic resources into its relatively least efficient, rather than more efficient, sectors. Tariff actions based on relative costs of production in different countries are therefore invalid as appropriate guides for tariff policy. In the broader perspective of stages of economic development and relative advantage in the world division of labor, such policies are indefensible and can only lead to world disorganization.

Much of the literature emphasizing the need for balanced growth in the economic development of countries appears to imply that the full range of production capabilities must be possessed by the individual countries. However, the stages of growth theory encompasses a shifting pattern of imports and exports due to shifts in comparative advantage at different stages of country development. The theory indicates how specialization and a world division of labor, along with increased international trading, can provide balanced growth for the world economic system and substantially reduces the need for balanced growth among individual countries.

Often long-range projections for individual countries are based on the product and production patterns of the country at its given stage of development. When the probable evolution of product patterns as the nation moves to higher stages of economic development are taken into account, the projection of both the quantity and composition of production, consumption, exports and imports must be substantially modified.

An additional value of the framework is in the historical perspective it provides from the standpoint of an understanding of the time phasing of the development of individual sectors. There is a tendency on the part of businessmen to extrapolate into the future whatever has occurred in the recent past. As a consequence, errors in long-range planning inevitably follow.

The focus of this study is on long-range business planning. The stages of growth theory do not encompass all aspects of short-run business fluctuations. However, it provides a valuable framework even for short-run decisions. The severity of economic fluctuations is aggravated in industries in which growth rates have declined. Rapidly growing industries virtually swamp the adverse cyclical swings. Furthermore, product-market planning to mitigate cyclical declines must also relate to longer-run growth trends. Firms which add new product lines which have exhibited historical stability may be entering new markets in which future sales volume may show either slow growth or secular declines.

One of the great values of the great historical perspective provided by the framework is that it should give a businessman a useful perspective for understanding government policy. Certain things are appropriate and feasible for government policy in the early stages of the country's economic development. Other policies are likely to be highly expensive in terms of effective applications of the country's resources. This is particularly important in the lower stages of the country's development when there is a tendency to attempt to encompass too many capabilities too soon. Conversely, at the higher stages of a nation's development, the more grievous error is likely to continue to support the flow of resources into industries which on the basis of continued developments in the world division of labor call for decreases in growth rates for these individual industries.

As the broad framework suggests, there are differential growth rates for different industries at different stages of a nation's economic development. Taken together positive and negative growth rates for a group of industries can result in attractive, viable and healthy growth rates for the economy as a whole.

2

THE DATA PROBLEM IN THE UNDER-DEVELOPED OR EMERGING COUNTRIES

HERBERT W. ROBINSON

President, C.E.I.R. Inc., Washington, D.C.

THERE is great danger that the great potential of management sciences in contributing to the more rapid advancement of the economies of the underdeveloped or emerging countries will not be effectively exploited unless fully as much effort is invested in solving the data problems connected with the application of such sciences as is spent in developing techniques and modes of application themselves.

The tools of management sciences all involve measurements of variables and the interrelationships among these variables. For example, one of these tools, quantitative economics, deals with the allocation of scarce resources among competing needs in optimum ways. This requires measurements of the amount of resources which are available, the amount of a given resource which must be applied to achieve a specified unit of production or output, and measures of the contribution of this output in achieving the stated economic objectives. It is important in planning the best use of resources for the country to have reliable data on the resources themselves, the technological possibilities in combining these resources, and measures of the opportunities of trade with other countries.

Like so many other things, it is more important in statistics to have quality than quantity. We are recognizing this more and more

34

in the United States, and in recent years have made substantial progress toward the improvement of statistical definitions, their coverage and reliability, and in the elimination of some of the overlap and inconsistencies in our statistical programs. We have also placed more attention on the organization and timely presentation of these statistics so that they may be properly interpreted and used to the best advantage. The advent of the electronic computer, of course, has advanced both of these objectives tremendously. In addition, developments in the design of samples have enabled us to collect needed measures much more efficiently than before. In fact, we have found many instances where information based on samples is significantly more accurate than results obtained by complete enumeration. We are truly reaching the stage where we are making statistics work for us rather than being slaves to mountains of data.

Unfortunately, many of the approaches of management sciences demand data in a form in which it is not presently available. It is important that an attack be made on the data problem if the full benefits of more scientific methods of programming and implementing economic development programs are to be reaped. First, it is extremely important that basic economic data on such countries—both regular series and censuses—be developed on the basis of scientific statistical principles. This will be extremely difficult in the agricultural area but there should be much less of a problem in the industrial area, especially in the case of advanced technologies as opposed to handicrafts. In addition to more comprehensive and reliable official statistics and private statistics, it is important that techniques and practical methods of sampling be devloped for the purpose of collecting vital data essential to the application of management science techniques. This involves the training of resourceful statisticians within the government and private industry in the underdeveloped countries. It also involves such countries obtaining the services both on a full-time and on a consultant part-time basis of experts with extremely practical and well-rounded backgrounds in the development of statistics and other data from fragmentary information.

It is important, therefore, that in the development of a program to apply management sciences vigorously to the problems of the underdeveloped countries that a definite program be established by the United Nations, by the emerging country itself, by countries giving aid such as the United States, and by large industrial concerns operating in these territories, to assist these countries in the development of useful statistics and data, their effective assembly and orderly arrangement, and the assembly of important technological relationships regarding capacity presently installed.

A second prong of the attack is the development of up-to-date technological coefficients for use generally. This suggests the possible functions of the World Bank, the United Nations, and possibly industrial trade associations, in developing standardized sets of coefficients that are applicable generally to the more modern technologies being incorporated in the plants being erected in underdeveloped countries. We must appreciate the fact that such technology is to a considerable degree the same no matter where it is installed and that resulting economies of statistical effort are possible. An extensive amount of work has been completed in the development of technological coefficients for use in input–output and linear programming models. Many of these coefficients are applicable to the emerging technologies of the underdeveloped countries if developed and used at the production process level of detail. For example, basic chemical processes are much the same regardless of where the facilities are constructed. It is true that there are differences in the fuels used and in the auxiliary equipment for materials handling and related activities. However, a large body of such coefficients are becoming available through the development and application of input–output techniques to a large number of countries. By carefully selecting these coefficients for their applicability, they may be used in the construction of economic models for the emerging countries. The same is true for a body of other statistics including capital output ratios, consumption coefficients, learning curves, and many others.

One of the most important exports which the developed countries can send to the emerging countries is know-how in the statistical sciences, i.e. the efficient collection and use of statistical information. It is somewhat ironic that at the same time that we have learned to get along efficiently with a smaller relative volume of statistics by using information more selectively and by collecting it more efficiently through the use of samples, we are at the same time able to handle larger volumes through the use of electronic computers This represents a twofold advance in capacity to utilize statistical information. It is possible to collect and process so much more data and, at the same time, more leverage is obtained from the amount collected and processed. If this know-how can be transmitted to the emerging countries, it can mean a tremendous head start for them. Students of economic development know that the process of development need not be a repetition of historical patterns but instead may be vastly speeded up by the advantage of the technology of the times and the environment in the rest of the world. This is no less true for the technology of management sciences than for other technology. Perhaps in no other field of endeavor is our potential contribution to the advances of the underdeveloped countries greater.

A large amount of work, of course, is being done in the development and co-ordinating of statistical programs for the emerging countries. This includes the work of the United Nations, the World Bank, the countries themselves, and the developed countries offering aid to these countries. The United States, for example, has sent many statistical missions to these countries, comprised of experts from government or industry, under the auspices of the International Corporation Administration, now the Agency for International Development. Other countries, of course, have given similar assistance. The United Nations has organized a large effort in statistical collection and publication. Its economic commissions for various areas of the world have developed strong statistical programs. Some efforts have gone much beyond this. The Economic Commission for Latin America (ECLA), for example, has pioneered in the development of economic models useful in ascertaining the potential development paths that various countries are likely to take.

D

Such models are useful to investors in forecasting future demand and in estimating the potential market for various industrial products.

It is very important that these efforts be extended and expanded. For very modest resources, the experience and know-how in the management sciences of the developed countries can be made available to the less-developed countries. It is difficult to imagine an area of endeavor in which the pay-off would be larger or the leverage of the invested dollar greater. This is the challenge to the members of the management sciences professions to contribute to the development of these countries and to help raise the standard of living of the whole world.

3

THOUGHT PROCESSES AND NEW TOOLS OF PLANNING FOR THE DEVELOPING COUNTRIES

MICHEL VERHULST

Maître de Recherche au Centre National de la Recherche Scientifique et Professeur à l'École Nationale des Ponts et Chaussées, Paris

AT THE beginning of the report[1] of the United Nations Committee for Industrial Development, to conclude its First Session (27 March 1961), three groups of problems are mentioned as having special importance for the newly developing countries. The first group relates to the transfer of technology and its adaptation to conditions different from those prevailing in the more advanced countries. The second group has to do with the choice of industrialization policies for which "a systematic statistical and analytical study of the various problems involved might make it possible to avoid many serious miscalculations".[2] The essential problem of the integration of industrial projects into an overall economic plan falls also into this category, the main point being in this case "to find relationships which would permit

---

[1] U.N. document E/3476, 24 April 1961.

[2] Ibid., The report adds at this point:

"In the planning and execution of the technical assistance programmes, the United Nations had always recognized and stressed the specific character of each situation and problem; that did not mean, however, that experience and analysis covering a great many specific cases could not provide a basis for generalizations of value both to governments and to industrial managers."

the integration of macro-economic and micro-economic approaches into simple homogeneous concepts[1]." It was felt that "there is a need, both in planning and at the implementation stage, for an over-all approach that brought together the various disciplines concerned."[1] Finally, a third group of problems has to do with the consequences on the world economy of the industrialization of the newly developing countries. In this respect "economic projections had become a major requirement of modern international life",[1] especially "in regions where population pressures and the scale of the problems to be contended with left little room for errors of calculation."[2]

Now, the scientific-minded economists and the specialists of the management sciences (and of operations research) will recognize immediately that they have something to offer for the solution of these problems, *especially for the second type of problem*, the formulation of which, as given in the report, follows very closely some of the conclusions arrived at by the experts of the Operations Research Consulting Group which met *informally* at the United Nations Headquarters on 30–31 January 1961.

In fact, the three first paragraphs of the *Statement of Conclusions* arrived at by the experts who participated in the consultation read as follows:

> 1. Operations research, a methodological approach that complements various substantive disciplines, provides powerful tools for solving important problems of decision making encountered in the industrialization of newly developing countries.
>
> 2. This approach is applicable at various levels of economic aggregation. For individual enterprises and industrial complexes, techniques already employed in relatively developed countries are readily adaptable. For development planning at the national level, operations research is applicable in principle and represents an extension of available methodology of economic programming. In particular, it facilitates the systematic integration of micro- and macro-system studies, and has demonstrated its potentialities in solving problems of industrialization in Argentina, Brazil, Israel, Mexico, Puerto Rico, U.A.R., and other countries, especially in the context of national development planning.

[1] Ibid., p. 6

[2] Ibid., p. 6. According to the report, the foreign trade sector seems to provide a good example of this type of problem.

3. The operations research approach provides logical guide lines for the collection of economic and other relevant data within a versatile framework and the availability of such a statistical system facilitates in turn the application of such techniques as simulation, linear programming, inter-industry analysis and queueing theory in raising the productivity of available capital, labor, and material resources.

It is these conclusions which serve as *background for the present paper*, and we hope that they might stimulate further research.

Naturally, each country has specific problems, and it would be a mistake to think that operations research is a panacea which can solve all problems. It is useful, however, to list some of them, as an indication of the areas in which the new methods might be useful.[1] Most of these problems have to do with planning in one form or another and this is the reason why we have chosen this theme as subject matter for the present paper.

We will start by saying *why planning is necessary* in the newly developing countries. We will then say a few words on *the thought process going on in planning*, whether it is done on a large scale or only in view of eventual emergencies. We will finally concentrate on *some of the new tools and techniques* which show particular promise of being very useful for planning purposes.

There is no doubt that technological progress has been the main motivation of economic development in the industrialized countries and that capital formation in the form of equipment and machinery was the consequence of the successive waves of creativity in the field of technology. This industrial revolution resulted in economic development and brought the industrialized countries at the point where they are today. But since it is of the nature of science to open new fields for discoveries and inventions at an ever-increasing pace, signs of a second industrialized revolution through automation become more and more apparent. Technological progress, however, depends now on teamwork and proper organization, and one of its outward manifestations is the emerging power of managers.

[1] See Appendix I (p. 52) for this list of suggestions.

Managers plan, organize, staff, direct, and control. But planning comes first, especially long-range planning, this new function which proves itself more and more useful in the big corporations of the industrialized countries.

Planning is all pervasive. It leads, for instance, to a more refined analysis of the environment in which operates the economic unit, but it achieves its purpose through the detail planning which becomes possible once the master plan has been developed.

Naturally, feedback effects play their role as soon as actual execution of the plans has started. Attempts at implementation bring more information on which the planners can rely for improving the plans. Information is the raw material of planning, but the job of the planner is to process and structure the information in such a way that it becomes meaningful and suitable for action.

It is not surprising, therefore, that economic planning at the national level should be felt desirable by the governments of most countries, especially the newly independent countries. Some sort of planning is felt necessary, and rightly so, in order to stay in power and obtain economic results. But the question is whether planning is feasible in practice at that level.

The question of feasibility can be decided on by reference to what is being done in countries like the U.S.S.R., Poland, India, etc., which practise some form of central planning, and by countries like the United States which believe in planning at the level of the big corporations but also practise it, to some extent, at the national level through the federal budget, and at the local level through various forms of planning. But one should make a distinction between planning viewed as a thought process and operational planning. At the national level it is mostly the thought process which is accepted at present by the industrialized countries, with perhaps the exception of France. There is no doubt, however, that planning will become more and more operational at the national level when new methods of planning will have been developed. It is this more advanced form of planning that we call *operational planning*.

Planning is also felt necessary by the governments of the newly independent countries because they cannot go through the historical pattern of industrial development which countries like the United States have experienced in the past. Traditionally, the flow of cash and the credits obtained and repaid by the exports of natural products financed the first phases of industrialization. To some extent this pattern repeats itself for countries such as Ghana which, in spite of their almost complete dependence on exports of one or two products (cocoa, coffee, tea, minerals), managed to achieve considerable recognition and stability because they are in a position to finance economic expansion with minimum outside help. But this is not the general case. Not mentioning the price element,[1] the probable increase in international trade for foodstuffs and agricultural raw materials over the next 15 years is not as good as the estimated corresponding increase for minerals and mineral fuels, and this may lead to great difficulties in the case of countries which export mostly agricultural products. Furthermore, the acceleration of technological progress plays in favour of the industrialized countries, although there are means to adapt technological knowledge to the particular needs of the less industrialized countries.

It seems, however, that the main discoveries which are necessary and will be made in order to narrow the gap in the economic structures of the two types of countries will not be of a technological nature. They will be of an institutional and organizational nature. The function of planning, for instance, will come more to the fore, and its importance will be more and more recognized. New tools will also be developed in order to make planning feasible and practicable at all levels of responsibility.

The present paper concentrates on the thought process of planning but draws also the attention to some new tools and techniques which appear particularly promising for planning purposes. As such, it may serve as a basis for discussion and *eventual development of programs of research in the field of operational planning.*

---

[1] Prices of primary commodity exports are very sensitive to changes in demand and this creates great difficulties for the less industrialized countries.

Planning viewed as a thought process is essentially long range in nature. One could say that there is a sort of duality between the objectives of long-range planning and the plans which make them become a reality. The actual implementation of the plans, however, reveals whether the objectives are realistic or not. Minor difficulties of implementation are surmounted easily, but structural difficulties either call for drastic new means of implementation or force to change the objectives. This operational way of finding realistic objectives and of ironing out the difficulties which are encountered in the actual implementation of the plans creates also the conditions for a smooth and balanced pattern of development.

Any planning system, however, must operate by reference to some criteria of performance. In other words, means must be found to measure the operational effectiveness of the system. This term, readily used by the military, is for them a compound of strategy, state of training, and logistics,[1] and a planning system is worth developing only if it brings improvements to the state of affairs which exists already.

In the field of economic development, this implies that value criteria can be established in terms, for instance, of output *per capita*, utilization of national resources, productivity of capital or of labour, rate of return on investment, saving in imports, accumulation of foreign exchange, etc. Naturally, the criteria and their respective weights in the value function vary according to the systems under consideration.

Some theoretical problems encountered in planning, such as the problem of the optimum allocation of resources under some side conditions, and many other problems for which the techniques of "linear programming" can be used, assume that the value function is

[1] See "Risk and Hazard in Logistics Planning", by H. A. Sachaklian, *Naval Logistics Research Quarterly*, **2**, 4 (December 1955). For this author: "Strategy is a scheme of manoeuver expressed as a series of decisions concerning the employment and deployment of armed forces. State of training is the level of the collective skill of the armed forces in carrying out these decisions. Logistics is the provision of the resources required by the strategy as conditioned by the state of training."

given. This means that the criteria and their relative weights are known, in which case it is possible to talk of maximizing the value function subject to certain constraints.

In our opinion, this procedure is misleading when the real problem is to find an operational way of discovering the shape of the value function, i.e. to find procedures which will make people agree on the criteria and the weights to take into account. Take the problem, for instance, of the allocation of a lump sum to the poor villages of a district when there are political considerations to consider. The way to a solution could be to make the authorities decide on the criteria which characterize a poor village, establish a list of the relevant ones, and ask them to establish scales of preference by giving weights of importance to the criteria. The solution of the allocation problem will follow but, in the light of the consequences, the scales of preference will probably have to be readjusted, and this will lead to another solution. Finally, through this process of trial and error, a general compromise will be obtained and the shape of the value function will be known. Naturally, the problem of how to make people agree on a set of criteria is not a pure economic problem, but it may be the most difficult problem to solve in practice.

Another point to consider for planning purposes is whether enough information is available or can be collected at a reasonable cost. No detailed planning is possible without concrete and precise information. Collecting the proper kind of information is almost as important as making people agree on the criteria of performance. This means that the countries which do not have a proper statistical system and are not able to supply good and relevant statistics should create one.

Furthermore, information from other countries should also be obtained in order, for instance, to choose the right kind of technology and determine the appropriate scale of operations when investments are at stake. Classifications of equipment according to the needs and the sources of supply will be particularly useful, and tables of unit requirements according to types of manufacturing in terms of plant investment, labour, power, materials, etc., should be compiled. This kind of information will help when it comes to ranking investment projects. All projects may be desirable but they cannot all be started immediately because of the shortage of resources or of their effect on external indebtedness.[1]

One type of planning which should be developed, whether full-scale planning is desirable or not, is *contingency planning*. It aims at making full use of the scarce resources which should be kept in reserve in order to face emergencies and smooth out the bad consequences of events external to the system. These events are usually not recurrent and have no influence on the basic objectives of the plan. Bottlenecks, if they are not too serious, have this nature, and it is important to have a planning system which detects bottlenecks and anticipates their consequences. More generally, contingency planning proposes plans for various types of contingencies, including the errors in planning which can be corrected.

In contingency planning, the planner is like a player in a game against Nature. He wants to play safe, but he wants to play. He must take risks, but he is very often in a position to build up an organization which will produce at a given time the course of action which is appropriate to the circumstances.

To identify the structure of the game, to determine the various possible courses of action opened to the player, and to select the best course of action in case of emergency is the main mission of people engaged in contingency planning.

A review of the *new tools and techniques* which offer some promise of a breakthrough for economic planning purposes is now in order. But we will limit ourselves to the tools which make use of the simulation methods because this approach, although still in the pioneering stage, follows very closely the philosophy of planning developed in the present paper.

---

[1] Professor Frisch has developed a method of program evaluations which shows how the problem can be tackled. See "Optimal Investments under Limited Foreign Resources", by Ragnar Frisch, *Memorandum of the Institute of Economics* (University of Oslo, 1959).

Simulation methods are simply a form of controlled experimentation on the model of a system. The principal advantages of simulation are the ability to control inputs to the system model, ease of recording system outputs, and speed of computation when the programs have been completed for use by a computer. The essential steps in any simulation are those of model building and experimental design, the latter showing which runs to make on the computer. The simulation results provide a way to test indirectly the macroscopic laws which govern the system and to see whether the model is a valid model of the real system.

In any simulation, the starting point is then the macroscopic models and the analytical studies which suggest various significant structures for the system. For instance, in an attempt at simulation of a system of industrial planning for investments in a newly independent country, what is required is a set of rules for selecting the projects. Policies which might be considered jointly or alternatively for doing so could be the following:

(a) invest in fields which will maximize income over time and permit maximum utilization of abundant factors such as unskilled labour, land and native raw materials;
(b) invest in fields which will bring the largest return in funds for re-investment (directly through profits and depreciation allowances and indirectly through taxes) and maximize savings;
(c) invest in fields (fertilizers, ...) which will help maintain the subsistence level of the population in terms of basic necessities (food, clothing, ...) and allow for the explosive increase in population.

There are also numerous conditions to take into account. For instance, one should make sure that the technology purchased abroad with foreign exchange will not become rapidly obsolete, since an investment which uses a large amount of foreign exchange should provide a technology which will stay competitive with the technology developed in the industrialized countries. Furthermore, the question of timing of disbursements of foreign exchange might be crucial and a method of scheduling the operations associated with the investments should be found. Exogenous influences would also enter the problem in the form of possible delays, bad weather, change in prices of primary commodities exported, etc.

All these aspects could be incorporated into a model of the economy considered as a whole and the effects of the various policies for investments could be investigated in order to facilitate the final choice of the projects which should be undertaken.

The problem is then to experiment with the models and to consider the various policies simultaneously in order to find the effects of their interactions. Various situations marked by uncertainty and dynamic change could also be studied. This second phase of the studies comes when the phase of model building has been completed. But the great advantage of simulation over the analytical and more abstract types of models which the economists have considered in the past is that it allows for very detailed and concrete types of models, as detailed as required, for obtaining an accurate picture of the real system.

At this stage, an experimental design should be developed, since the simulation is conducted through a series of runs on the computer, each run corresponding to a particular case of behaviour of the system. The selection of the appropriate runs is a significant technical problem. These runs produce time-histories and data which are analyzed in order to understand the macroscopic behaviour of the system. This analysis is the most difficult part of the whole process and it is found necessary, very often, to use smaller analytical models in order to test the stability of the result over a wider range of parameters or variables than those used in the simulation.[1]

One should note also that the question of finding an optimum is secondary in a simulation study. What matters is to find the consequences of the various policies which can be considered and to take into account the possible manifestations of the external environment which may influence the system. When the overall behaviour of the

[1] These last comments were made to the author by Dr. Murray Geisler, the Rand Corporation.

system is known, it becomes possible to improve the policies and to come out with an integrated plan of action.

This approach has already been used in some projects but it has not yet been completely successful when the problems studied were of the type just described. There is no doubt, however, that the approach is powerful and that it is very fruitful in some fields. The military, for instance, have made extensive use of simulation, especially for war gaming and for simulating the behaviour and operation of logistics systems associated with the missions of the armed forces.[1]

In the field of economic planning, an interesting project was conducted by Dr. E. P. Holland, at the Center for International Studies of the Massachusetts Institute of Technology. The project is a Computer Study of Economic Take-off Problems in an economy similar to the Indian economy. The main objective of the study is to compare the effectiveness in an economy of different kinds of economic policies and programs intended to promote continuing growth of real income while avoiding undesirable side effects. To insure relevance to some actual problems, the principal model studied has been patterned on the economy of India. This model has been completely formulated, statistics on the Indian economy have been carefully studied to determine suitable values of parameters, and the program of investigation has been carried out.[2]

But there are other important studies which have been done, for instance, at C.E.I.R., on the economy of Puerto Rico, and at the University of Wisconsin, on the household sector of the United States economy. The latter project is under the direction of Guy H. Orcutt who was certainly one of the first pioneers in the field.[3]

---

[1] The Rand Corporation has published numerous reports in this field.

[2] See "Simulation of an Economy with Development and Trade Problems", by E. P. Holland, *The American Economic Review*, **52**, No. 3, (June 1962).

[3] See *Microanalysis of Socio-economic Systems: A Simulation Study*, by Guy H. Orcutt and associates, Harper, 1961. Also, by the same author, "Simulation of Economic Systems", *The American Economic Review*, **50**, No. 5, (December 1960).

A particular type of problem which should be mentioned as well has to do with the planning and the designing of multi-unit, multi-purpose water resource systems. A Water Resources Program,[1] for instance, was set up at Harvard University under the direction of Robert Dorfman.

There were three major objectives for the pilot study:

(i) to allow for the simultaneous consideration of a large number of alternative system designs;

(ii) to improve methodology for the planning of river systems so as to "marry" engineering and economics;

(iii) to improve methodology for the designing in order to adapt it to any reasonable institutional constraints.

The study has been quite successful and could be applied now to concrete cases.

In Great Britain, the simulation of a complex river system (the Nile Valley Plan) was done to help assess the relative merits of different reservoir systems for use in irrigation.[2] One of the research workers who had more to do with the programmation of the study, Dr. M. P. Barnett, is now in charge of the Co-operative Computing Laboratory of the Massachusetts Institute of Technology.

These are some of the tools and techniques which show promise of

[1] See *Design of Water Resources Systems*, by A. Maass *et al.* (Harvard University Press, Cambridge, Mass., 1962).

See also "Report on the Harvard Program of Research in Water Resources Development", by Arthur Maass and Maynard M. Hufschmidt, in *Resources Development, Frontiers for Research*, Papers of the Western Resources Conference, 1959 (University of Colorado Press, Boulder, 1960). See further "Design of the Simple Valley Project", by R. Dorfman, *Proceedings of the Symposium on the Economics of Watershed Planning* (Tennessee Valley Authority, Knoxville, Tennessee). This symposium took place on 10–12 June 1959. See finally "Choosing among Alternative Public Investments in the Water Resources Field" by Peter O. Steiner, *The American Economic Review*, **49,** No. 5, (December 1959).

[2] See "Planning for the Ultimate Hydraulic Development of the Nile Valley", by Humphrey Alan Walter Morrice and William Nimmo Allan, *Proceedings of the Institution of Civil Engineers* (*London*), October 1959 and July 1960.

leading to a better understanding of planning. To start using them it is not necessary to have direct access to a computer, at least not in the first stages of the studies, those concerned with model building. But these studies should be undertaken with the idea that what really matters is to understand the behaviour of the systems described by the models. The ability to take the right decisions will then be enhanced because the consequences of the decisions will have become apparent.

To sum up, simulation methods as applied to operational planning will become a powerful tool for predicting effects completely unthought of. Complex policies will be tried before being applied, and forecasting will become more of a science.[1] In fact any forecast is the result of a simulation since it is made by reference to a model. In turn, the quality of the model can be appraised through the quality of the forecast. If the results are not valid, it means that the structure of the model is not sound or that the parameters have not been estimated properly through lack of good information. The simulation provides, however, a sort of feedback mechanism which shows what must be done in order to improve the quality of the model. In a way, then, economic systems offer some analogies with the systems studied by control engineers. But the real difficulties come from the cost and scarcity of information and from the impossibility of systematic experimentation. Model building and simulation are the operational way to go around these difficulties but, at the same time, they give a good basis for better planning.[2]

[1] For an example see "An Operational Approach to the Problems of Forecasting", by Michel Verhulst, *Proceedings of the Pilot Clinics on the Impact of Feedback Control Concepts in the Study of Economic and Business Systems* (F.I.E.R., New York, 1961).

[2] To complement this approach, we give in Appendix II some comments by Francis W. Dresch of the Stanford Research Institute.

APPENDIX I

Some Suggestions[1] regarding the Practical Applications of Operations Research to the Problems of Industrialization of Newly Developing Countries (Examples)

Brazil

In the last 10 years the capital-intensive industries, such as basic chemicals, fertilizers, etc., have experienced a growth in output ranging from 75 to 150 per cent. The application of operations research techniques would be particularly useful to improve the utilization of installed capacity, and identify bottlenecks of further growth.

Peru

In connection with the overall economic plan to develop new areas for agricultural cultivation and to establish local industries, operations research techniques would be particularly appropriate to identify the most suitable sites for industrial centers, developing at the same time the most desirable network pattern for such centers.

Uruguay

Operations research would be a unique instrument to search for opportunities for further industrial development and diversification of international trade in a country with a highly developed education and a relatively small population limiting the local market possibilities.

India

Under the third Five Year Plan, it is contemplated to develop vigorously certain capital-intensive branches of industry (e.g. aluminum: 340 per cent increase in 1965/66 over 1960/61; paper and

[1] In Yap Kie Han, Director of the C.B.O. Centre for Management and Industrial Development, Rotterdam, is largely responsible for these remarks.

52

paper products: 120 per cent in the same 5-year period). In relation to these objectives, operations research techniques would be of great use to determine suitable plant locations, estimate the most economical investments for the different plants, and schedule the operations relative to the implementation of the new factories (or the expansion projects of existing enterprises).

Republic of China

In the past 10 years the manufacturing industries have developed at a high rate. To stimulate further growth which will depend, to a large extent, upon export trade, branchwise operations research studies would be particularly suitable. They would refer to the analysis of a complex of factors such as analysis of markets, pricing and cost problems, inventory and production-control, etc.

United Arab Republic

In view of the present concentration of population in the Nile Valley and along the coast, and also regarding the plans for multi-purpose and other economic development projects, operations research could make an important contribution in analyzing the transportation factors related to the establishment of industrial estates and the location of future industrial centers. An analysis could also be made of the demand on the transport services created by the economic development plan.

Newly Independent Countries of Africa

The newly independent countries will have to develop an industrialization strategy in order to plan their economic growth. In a great number of instances this can be done on the basis of a "common-sense approach", taking into account obvious indicators. In a few instances, however (e.g. large-scale investments for the development of a primary-metals industry), a more careful analysis would be advisable. Operations research provides the instruments to investigate alternative possibilities in relation to the overall pattern of development and to study the optimum mix of projects.

E

APPENDIX II

Potential Applications of Operations Research in Problems of Industrialization of Newly Developing Countries

By Francis W. Dresch
Stanford Research Institute

The problems associated with the industrialization of newly developing countries are not intrinsically different from the problems of development programming generally. Required for the study of such problems is a multi-pronged approach involving the construction of adequate theory, devising experimental tools for refining and testing this theory, and establishing methods for the practical application of this theory to the preparation of development programs. In such research, the theory will be essentially modern economic theory, both in the form of macro-economic theory of the whole economy and in the form of micro-economic theory of the individual enterprise or development project. The only conceivable experimental tool is some form of simulation, that is, quantitative examination of the consequences of alternative development programs under realistic constraints and under alternative assumptions about the environment in which the problem is embedded. Such experimentation can be used (1) to establish information requirements by testing the sensitivity of various anticipated outcomes to errors in data, (2) to evaluate whole series or classes of alternative policies, (3) to select alternatives that best satisfy relevant selection criteria, (4) to predict in detail the requirements and consequences of the programs favored. The need in development programming is a method for mass-producing integrated feasibility studies complete with capital requirement schedules and other essentials as well as quantitative forecasts of annual benefits.

It is suggested that the methods of operations research can be applied to the preparation of such systematic studies of feasibility.

The methods of operations research as applied to industrial problems are very similar to the methods of economic analysis, sharpened perhaps by a strong preference for quantitative formulations. The emergence of operations research as a new discipline distinct from conventional economic analysis has had to await the appearance of the high-speed computer which has made possible a quantitative approach to complex problems. One general technique that has been inseparably associated with industrial operations research has been computer simulation, through which numerical experimentation has been substituted for real-life experimentation. It must be admitted that much nonsense has been perpetrated in the name of simulation when it has been used as a substitute for sound analysis. The fact remains, however, that simulation can be used as an adjunct to hard thinking to explore complex nets of alternatives that would be hopelessly inaccessible to pure analysis. It is this two-pronged approach to the problems of development analysis plus simulation, that seems to offer the greatest potential for avoiding many unwise planning decisions if not for accurately anticipating the judgments of history.

To illustrate the potential advantages of such methods, it might be well to outline in a crude and preliminary form how one might use them to attack the most complex problem in national development, namely the preparation, analysis, and evaluation of a full spectrum of alternative development projects. The whole approach can be sketched in terms of a sequence of steps or phases through which the problem is formulated in a suitable analytic setting, classes of decision alternatives are identified, the consequences of alternative policies are anticipated, and criteria are developed for comparative evaluation of otherwise acceptable plans of action. To give the illustration some concreteness, let us assume that our goal is to prepare a feasible (and hopefully an optimal) plan for guiding the development of a rapidly developing country. This must be done within the political and social constraints imposed by law and custom, and in a free enterprise economy which imposes limitations on the incentives that are amenable to manipulation by a planning authority. The suggested approach might be described in the following ten steps to be pursued somewhat sequentially although some obvious overlapping and recycling will be appropriate.

1. *Describing the Current Situation.* As a first step in the preparation of an adequate inventory of the resources of the country, include natural resources, industrial, and other productive capacity, labor force by skills and professional education. Also this should include significant geographical data on location of facilities and resources particularly with respect to waterways, railheads, highway, and communication links if any; distances involved, as well as general conditions of terrain; and other factors affecting accessibility. In general, this step collects and complements available data on the current situation in descriptive or statistical form. Obvious gaps in data that cannot be filled in readily are noted for future reference.

2. *Identifying Candidate Projects.* The second step is the preparation of an adequate list of reasonable development projects. This list should include as many projects as are at all plausible either nominated by individuals, suggested by the assessment of the current situation, or by foreign developments. At this point an effort should be made to avoid any tendency towards undue haste in prejudging the desirability, urgency, or feasibility of these proposals. Some attempt to group or classify them might be desirable, however.

3. *Estimating Costs and Requirements.* After combining proposals where possible into variants on basic propositions, and eliminating inadmissible ones, very crude cost engineering studies can be conducted on those remaining. Time-phased requirements for capital and specialized resources should be estimated as well as expected benefits, requirements, and the scope or scale of projects.

4. *Identifying Limitations Imposed by the Economy.* Use available

input–output models or construct other aggregate econometric models of the current economy and its current rate of growth. Such models put limits on the possible rate of capital accumulation from internal or external sources and describe the basic structure of the economy. This step will be used to determine any further limitations on the various factors involved in the specific development proposals or in the development plan.

5. *Estimating Market Potentials.* Make estimates of the potential markets for products or services under consideration, both internally and externally. Estimate the price sensitivity of these markets in the neighborhood of current or potential world prices, and note any history of special trading agreements restricting the terms of trade in these markets.

6. *Estimating Rate of Return.* Estimate potential returns from implementing specific proposals either in foreign exchange or in social values, as a function of the investment required. Eliminate enough of the least attractive proposals to bring aggregate requirements close to available resources.

7. *Building a Model.* Now synthesize a general plan from the remaining proposals. This can be done by leaving many variables unspecified, for example the size or scale of individual development projects or other quantities to be determined by planning decision. The result of this step is a model or quantitative description of alternative forms of the plan, each involving one or more of the elemental project proposals.

8. *Sensitivity Testing.* Simplify this model in any way possible to reduce it to a form suitable for computer experimentation; then develop the computer program necessary for evaluating alternatives or for testing the significance of earlier estimates of costs, benefits, and other factors in the various quantitative relations. The sensitivity testing is designed to identify critical factors requiring more accurate estimation and offer guidance in eliminating non-critical factors or relations that may be approximated to facilitate experimentation. Measures of benefits need not be in monetary terms but may

involve a variety of different quantitative results as anticipated consequences of a plan.

9. *Evaluation of Alternatives.* By comparative evaluation of alternative plans or by supplementary analysis, arrive at a preferred plan or
several most desirable plans.

10. *Verifying Feasibility of Final Plan.* Validate the foregoing
analysis and simulation by direct study of the favoured plan or plans.
Avoid approximations as much as possible and refine estimates to
complete a check on previous results. Work out detailed statements
of plan requirements and detailed schedules of implementation.
This could include identification of required legislation, tax, or other
incentives, or other policy decisions needed to insure successful outcome. This step ends the research and prepares the way for initiation
of all necessary action.

This ten-step procedure was described in terms of a desirable but
unattainable goal, the development of an optimal integrated plan for
a whole country. The same steps or recombinations of these can
more readily be applied to less ambitious development problems.
It is only in a very limited sense that the method insures optimal
solutions if indeed it ever does at all, but it does insure rationality and
feasibility as well as more than adequate planning effectiveness.

I do not wish to give the impression that simulation in this ten-
step version is the only technique of operations research that can be
applied to problems of development. Other more specific techniques
may be applicable to specific problems, such as facility location or
optimal rate of depletion of exhaustible resources. The simulation
approach contains within it much that is new in operations research
and has wide applicability for development planning. It can be
helpful in planning everything from a national education program
to a program for the development of a whole country. Its reliability
is no better than that of the input data, but the intrinsic capacity
for evaluating its own output not only can guide the research effort
but also can provide an excellent validation of plans formulated.
It does not eliminate the need for careful economic analysis or

general study of the full environment of constraints surrounding a planning problem. It does supplement such analysis, however, while providing a technique for organizing and facilitating research efforts in an efficient and, hopefully, in a fruitful manner. This is why simulation seems to provide the greatest potential for development planning.

4

PERSPECTIVES ET LIMITES DE L'INDU-STRIALISATION COMME SOLUTION AU PROBLÈME DU SOUS-DÉVELOPPEMENT DANS LES PAYS NEUFS

C. CROUZET

Ancien Directeur des Travaux Publics de la France d'Outre-Mer, Paris

ÉBLOUIS par les perspectives qu'ouvrent l'atome domestiqué, l'énergie solaire captée et les déserts irrigués, les jeunes états son, impatients de trouver une clef magique pour accéder sans tarder aux bénéfices de l'industrialisation. Dans leur impatience, ils ont tendance à se rattacher aux systèmes et idéologies qui leur paraissent rendre cet accès le plus facile. Il est donc essentiel pour les anciens colonisateurs de rechercher si ce qu'ils offrent est satisfaisant. Pour ce faire, nous commencerons par étudier *l'évolution de la doctrine* qui a présidé, dans le passé, aux relations économiques des nations évoluées et des pays sous-développés.

Ces relations furent historiquement dominées par la maîtrise et l'expansion de la technique. La maîtrise de la technique donnait la puissance et la possibilité pour celui qui la détenait de fixer uni-latéralement, à partir de ses seuls besoins propres et pratiquement à son seul profit, la nature de ces relations; mais son expansion, ayant universalisé le problème, oblige maintenant à trouver une solution susceptible de satisfaire en profondeur les aspirations des différents pays.

Le problème du tiers monde peut même se ramener maintenant au conflit de ces deux tendances, car, par nature, la seconde fait de plus en plus intervenir des forces internes éminemment dynamiques dans l'essor des pays sous-développés, alors que la première procède surtout à partir de moteurs et d'intérêts externes et apporte moins d'attention aux facteurs locaux de multiplication. De toutes façons, l'industrialisation sera un des éléments essentiels de la solution puisqu'elle constitue la fin économique de la science et de la technique.

Le problème des pays sous-développés a été posé à la civilisation européenne par le seul fait de leur découverte à la fin du Moyen-Age, lorsque certaines novations techniques comme la boussole, le gouvernail à étambot et la maîtrise de la voile, autorisant la navigation hauturière, eurent permis aux marins de l'Europe de faire reculer les "bords mystérieux du monde occidental".

Mais à l'époque, la taille et la façon des caravelles, en fonction de la technique d'alors, ne permirent aux conquistadors que d'aller chercher dans les pays neufs des épices et gemmes précieuses ainsi que le "fabuleux métal que Cipango mûrit dans ses rives lointaines". Toutefois l'or des Amériques, monopolisé à leur seul profit et à leur seule gloire par les dynasties ibériques, n'a eu, à considérer ses incidences historiques, qu'une influence éphémère et superficielle, infiniment plus faible que quelques faits techniques, alors obscurs, qui ont accompagné ces voyages des conquistadors et dont les prolongements restent actuels, importants et profonds, car devenus des moteurs internes des économies en cause. Il s'agit de l'introduction, en Europe, du tabac et de la pomme de terre et, en sens inverse, de l'implantation de la canne à sucre dans sa terre d'élection de Saint-Domingue et des Antilles.

Ce sont encore des faits techniques, comme l'augmentation de la taille des navires de mer et l'apparition de l'embryon de l'industrie européenne à partir du 17ème siècle (moment où se situe aussi l'apport du café et du cacao), qui ont conduit sinon à la conquête généralisée par l'Europe de ces terres lointaines, tout au moins à l'implantation de comptoirs plus ou moins étendus, et au démarrage des premiers échanges "commerciaux" appréciables. On put troquer des matières premières tropicales, encore réduites à quelques produits riches, contre des produits manufacturés européens: armes et pacotille.

Avec un tel esprit mercantiliste et un commerce ainsi conçu, la possession des terres lointaines devenait une source de richesses pour le pays qui les avait colonisées. Elles devenaient aussi, et ce fut vite le but recherché, une source de puissance si, avec l'essor industriel de l'Europe, le monopole d'une matière coloniale, en l'occurrence le coton, donnait aussi le monopole de la fabrication et du commerce des cotonnades.

Mais à ce jeu, l'Europe a, dès ce moment, suscité des réactions dans les colonies dont les intérêts ne furent pas pris en compte par la stratégie économique des métropoles. Pour avoir voulu tirer trop de profits des denrées qu'elle leur fournissait à partir de ses autres possessions, l'Angleterre fournit aux États-Unis un prétexte pour leur guerre d'indépendance. Et ce fut le point de départ du plus jaillissant essor économique connu, à partir du seul dynamisme des forces et des intérêts internes d'un pays nouveau.

Depuis le début du 19ème siècle, correspondant à un changement exponentiel d'échelle, la machine à vapeur et les progrès de la métallurgie et de l'architecture navale ont permis la construction de navires de mer d'une capacité et d'une économie telles que les matières premières tropicales accessibles se sont étendues progressivement des produits riches aux pondéreux. Ces nouveaux produits, oléagineux ou minerais, ont été de plus en plus recherchés par les industries métropolitaines qui sont devenues, dans une certaine mesure, dépendantes des pays dits aujourd'hui "pays à ressources".

On peut même dire que c'est à la fin du 19ème siècle que la facette "colonies fournisseurs de matières premières" a connu sa pleine expansion, et cela à une époque où le progrès des communications de tous ordres et le brassage des hommes acheminaient les pays neufs vers des prises de conscience de plus en plus précises.

L'expansion du commerce consécutive aux progrès de la technique, et l'accroissement des avantages qu'en retiraient les conquérants, conduisirent de plus, dès la fin du 19ème siècle, à une intensité plus grande des rivalités entre les grandes puissances. D'où la Conférence de Berlin de 1885, qui crut trouver dans le libre jeu de la concurrence commerciale internationale un remède bénéfique tant pour la paix du monde que pour les bonnes relations des colonisateurs et des colonisés. L'Acte de Berlin fit confiance aux bienfaits de la liberté et de la concurrence économiques pour assurer le mieux-être des populations locales et le développement de ces pays. De telles conceptions sont aujourd'hui dépassées mais il faut reconnaître que l'on atteignit par cette voie des résultats substantiels.

La position actuelle des pays à ressources ne change pas fondamentalement les rapports existant avec les nations fournisseurs de produits manufacturés. En effet, l'état de pays fournisseur de matières premières n'est pas confortable en l'organisation actuelle de l'économie du globe, car le cours de ces matières est fixé sur les marchés des grands centres utilisateurs, et leurs variations spéculatives ou autres sont amplifiées au stade de la valeur départ. Il n'est donc pas surprenant que les pays fournisseurs, gênés par la brutalité des fluctuations des cours, se préoccupent de s'y soustraire notamment en essayant de transformer leurs ressources propres pour élaborer des produits de consommation locale, et donc voient dans l'industrialisation, apothéose de la technique et fin de l'activité économique, le terme de leurs maux.

On a cru pouvoir dire qu'il n'y avait pas de dilemme entre l'industrialisation et la spécialisation dans la production des matières premières. Le Venezuela, par exemple, fournit une démonstration frappante d'une nation à ressources ayant atteint une base satisfaisante de développement. Mais l'origine de cette base est une production annuelle de plusieurs dizaines de millions de tonnes de pétrole, donc d'un tonnage suffisant pour que des "royalties", même modestes, procurent des recettes apréciables compte tenu du fait que le pétrole est une matière peu spéculative car monopolisée par un club très fermé de producteurs puissants.

Le cas, beaucoup plus général, des pays à productions différenciées de faible tonnage et à produits spéculatifs est très différent. De ce point de vue, l'exemple des États-Unis après leur indépendance mérite d'être médité. Après leur accès à l'indépendance, les États-Unis eurent recours à l'aide financière et technique européenne pour faire subir aux matières premières le cycle complet des transformations industrielles, et cela en fonction de leurs besoins propres et des nécessités de leur expansion. C'est ce merveilleux succès de l'Amérique que les pays neufs peuvent invoquer aujourd'hui pour prétendre à leur propre industrialisation.

Certes, scrupule politique ou défaut d'analyse, les africains ne mettent pas encore explicitement l'accent sur les avantages majeurs des moteurs internes de l'économie. Ceci facilite d'ailleurs la progressivité de l'évolution et le maintien des liaisons indispensables sur les plans techniques, commerciaux et financiers.

En fait, en face du conservatisme des métropoles, la doctrine politique actuelle des pays sous-développés repose maintenant sur les postulats suivants, tout au moins si l'on en juge par les positions prises à la conférence des pays africains d'expression française à la conférence de Brazzaville de janvier 1961:

Indépendance politique impliquant un pied d'égalité avec les pays industriels pour réaliser des échanges de services réciproques, ou le prétendre.

Importance de libérer l'économie des servitudes et des dangers de la brutalité des fluctuations à court et moyen terme des cours de la plupart des matières premières sur le marché mondial, car ces fluctuations ne permettent aucun plan à échéance raisonnable.

Transformation sur place au maximum des ressources du pays, tant pour l'exportation que pour la consommation locale, et cela quel que soit le prix de l'industrialisation nécessaire.

Ainsi, parce qu'ils y voient le terme de leurs maux, les nouveaux états indépendants ont tendance à tenir l'industrialisation pour le moyen essentiel de sortir de leur sous-développement et pour la clef magique de leur expansion, ajoutant ainsi un moteur national puissant à une tendance historique universelle. Mais si souhaitable et inéluctable que soit une pareille voie vers le progrès, nous allons voir, *en examinant les expériences déjà réalisées et en analysant les sujétions et les difficultés,* que cette évolution ne se fera pas sans mal. En effet, les servitudes qui grèvent la technique et la technologie pèsent très lourd, au départ, et elles perpétuent certaines conditions inhérentes aux anciens pactes coloniaux. *Au-delà de l'industrialisation, il faut donc chercher des solutions efficaces dans une action plus profonde, plus différenciée, et plus harmonisée,* action certes mue au principal de l'intérieur, mais nécessitant également une collaboration, sur tous les plans et à tous les stades, avec les pays étrangers.

Remarquons tout d'abord que le mythe de l'industrialisation est né dans les pays neufs en dehors de toute préoccupation économique. Ceci peut être facilement illustré par différents exemples.

Dans une Afrique à la géographie massive, les transports ont été le prétexte à la première manifestation de la technique, le génie militaire lançant à la suite de la conquête les voies ferrées de pénétration. Ces voies avaient avant tout pour but la maîtrise du pays, d'où des impératifs de rapidité et d'économie de construction. A partir d'un trafic nul et d'une vocation économique encore indéterminée, il ne pouvait être question ni de calculs de rentabilité ni de discussion des caractéristiques. Et pourtant, entre le trafic qu'elles permettaient et les possibilités du portage, il y avait un abîme tant pour le volume que pour le prix de revient des transports. Ces voies initiales ont donc été à l'origine de l'essor économique de ces pays et ont constitué le moyen de leur intégration au reste du monde. Il ne faut certes pas l'oublier aujourd'hui quelque manifestes que soient souvent les tares de ces chemins de fer, tares d'ailleurs plus réelles sur le plan des communications internes que sur celui des relations avec le monde extérieur. Et il ne faut pas oublier non plus qu'il y aura peu de réalisations industrielles qui apporteront, dans l'avenir, des éléments de mutation aussi puissamment efficaces. D'ailleurs, relativité des concepts humains, il est curieux de constater que les dépenses correspondantes, faites surtout à titre de souveraineté et ainsi condamnées dans leur principe par l'Acte de Berlin, constituent aujourd'hui l'un des héritages les plus gratuits et les plus bénéfiques à mettre au compte de l'actif moral des pays colonisateurs.

Il n'y eut pas d'impératifs économiques non plus à la production des matériaux de construction : moellons, tuiles, chaux, agglomérés, bois d'œuvre, etc., à laquelle durent se livrer, pour leur propre installation, les premiers colonisateurs. Quel que fut le prix de ces matériaux, il était infiniment moins élevé, vu leur masse et le coût des transports, que celui des matériaux importés. Il n'en est pour preuve que le rapide abandon des charpentes métalliques qui servirent d'ossature, presque partout, aux premiers bâtiments coloniaux. Pour les matériaux de construction, le seul problème au départ était de les produire, production étant alors synonyme à elle seule d'efficacité et d'économie.

Les préoccupations de rentabilité et de recherche de bas prix de revient ont été également exclues, à l'origine, de l'installation des industries créées pour fournir aux premiers occupants certains éléments de confort comme l'eau, la glace ou l'électricité, et laissées souvent pour ce motif, sous forme de régies, à la charge totale de la collectivité. Si l'on recourait aux concessions privées, elles étaient assorties soit de garanties fort complexes de résultats soit de tarifs substantiels comme celui prévu en 1905 pour l'électricité à Tananarive.

Il ne fut donc pas question alors d'une politique concertée pour stimuler le développement économique. Et pourtant, dès ce moment, ces réalisations de base, ateliers ferroviaires, production de matériaux de construction, distribution d'eau et d'électricité, concentrées dans les centres principaux où l'on pouvait aussi commencer à s'occuper efficacement, et à un prix abordable, des divers coûts de l'homme (santé, hygiène, enseignement, voirie, habitat, etc.), ont constitué, avec les réalisations faites à ce second titre, des points d'appui internes de l'essor économique, contribuant à fixer autour de ces points des îlots de prospérité. Leur potentiel ne fut, cependant, pas suffisant pour leur conférer à l'égard des autres activités un effet moteur et une capacité d'entraînement assez dynamiques. En outre, ce défaut fut d'autant plus réel qu'au départ l'environnement économique ne pouvait que difficilement s'accommoder d'activités correspondant aux seuils imposés par les nécessités techniques.

Mais malgré ces servitudes et la lenteur de démarrage de toute expansion à allure exponentielle, ces points d'appui initiaux ont fait cristalliser et croître autour d'eux des îlots de prospérité locaux où tout était plus facile que dans le reste du pays, l'action sociale comme le progrès économique. Aussi, malgré la résistance des isolés de la brousse qui s'estimaient défavorisés dans la distribution des ressources publiques, l'autorité prit progressivement conscience de leur rôle actif de levain interne, et l'on s'attacha toujours, sans trop s'encombrer de considérations de rentabilité, à accroître leur potentiel. C'est de ce point de vue notamment que l'on doit apprécier l'accent mis dans le premier plan de l'Outre-Mer français sur la politique d'énergie à bon marché dans les grands centres, politique qui visait à y attirer l'industrie. Toutefois, avec un programme comportant des centrales non interconnectées et qui anticipait largement sur le développement industriel, il fut nécessaire d'attendre au moins quelques années pour obtenir un complet équilibre financier. En face de ces déficits initiaux inévitables, il faut d'ailleurs mettre le bénéfice du succès de certains essors industriels différenciés, dont l'un des plus brillants exemples est, hors des territoires ex-français, celui de Léopoldville.

Le second départ de l'industrialisation des pays sous-développés a été pratiquement indépendant du premier processus, et il fut marqué par une beaucoup plus grande orthodoxie économique et financière du fait qu'il fut l'œuvre de groupes privés. Il s'agissait, en effet, de procéder à une première transformation des produits locaux non exportables à l'état brut: produits agricoles périssables comme le manioc, sorti d'abord séché puis sous forme de fécule ou de tapioca, ou comme la canne à sucre, et produits miniers à faible teneur, autour de 3% pour le minerai de nickel de Nouvelle Calédonie, alors que l'on exporte encore à l'état brut la bauxite ou certains minerais de fer à titre élevé, 45% et plus. Ces industries se sont établies sur le lieu de la ressource et non dans les centres préexistants et privilégiés.

Elles avaient d'autant plus à être rentables que, d'une part, elles avaient tout à créer et que, d'autre part, elles devaient compétitivement écouler leurs produits, soit sur le marché mondial, soit sur celui de leurs métropoles.

Mais l'on peut dire que si elles n'ont pas fixé à elles seules la vocation économique du pays où elles se sont établies, comme dans le cas du nickel de Nouvelle Calédonie ou du cuivre du Katanga, elles ont certainement puissamment contribué à définir cet avenir.

Aujourd'hui, quand les pays neufs africains accèdent à l'indépendance, ils héritent tant en équipements de base et activités induites, qu'en équipements autonomes de production ou de transformation, d'une infrastructure industrielle non négligeable, même si l'on peut questionner les intérêts en fonction desquels elle a été conçue. L'autonomie, surtout en l'absence de tout capital autochtone, amenera certainement ces pays à de nouveaux critères pour les choix industriels auxquels ils auront à procéder. Ils seront sans doute conduits à s'écarter à nouveau de strictes considérations de rentabilité, prétextant que l'intérêt national exige rapidement d'élargir la notion d'indépendance, pour que celle-ci devienne vraiment réelle. Nous touchons ici au stade de l'évolution qui comporte le plus de risques psychologiques et par conséquent politiques, confrontant la recherche de l'indépendance totale avec les sujétions des réalisations économiques et techniques.

Mais au lieu d'être matériellement isolés du reste du monde comme au début de la période coloniale, les pays sous-développés bénéficient maintenant d'une intégration appréciable de leur activité à celle de ce dernier. C'est donc en fonction de ces relations, et non *ex nihilo*, comme lors de la création des premiers équipements de base, qu'il faudra concevoir et réaliser, au moins dans une certaine mesure, les nouvelles installations industrielles. Mais quelle que soit la doctrine qui y présidera, la future industrialisation des pays sous-développés connaîtra, en fonction des liaisons existantes ou nécessaires avec l'extérieur, des servitudes techniques, économiques et financières qu'il importe maintenant d'analyser. Pour ce faire, *nous examinerons en premier lieu les contingences particulières aux industries de consommation locale, puis celles des activités exportatrices, et nous aborderons ensuite les problèmes communs.*

Pour les industries tournées vers les marchés intérieurs, les problèmes de seuil sont primordiaux, car quelle que soit la protection dont elles peuvent bénéficier au départ, les exigences techniques ne leur permettent d'être viables qu'au-delà d'un certain volume de production. Cette production limite ne peut être atteinte que si le marché et les besoins locaux desservis sont d'un volume adéquat. Or ce volume ainsi que ses variations dépendent de l'étendue de l'hinterland résultant de la géographie et du réseau des voies de communication, de la population correspondante, des conditions démographiques, et surtout des revenus et de leurs possibilités d'accroissement.

Liées ainsi à tous les éléments de l'expansion du pays, il est normal que, lorsqu'elles s'y créent, les industries de consommation locale, malgré les protections de douane et de change, connaissent dans ces régions des débuts difficiles, surtout si elles apparaissent dans une période de progrès limité, comme celle de l'entre-deux guerres; mais après ce début laborieux, et parce que l'esprit d'entreprise les aura créées à efficacité marginale, elles connaîtront un bel avenir. Il est normal aussi que ces industries de consommation locale ne naissent que progressivement et suivant un cheminement d'ailleurs assez constant, parce que conforme à l'évolution des besoins: ateliers mécaniques d'entretien et de construction, cimenteries, cotonnades, brasseries, entreprises frigorifiques, etc.

De façon générale, les dernières industries accessibles à un pays au cours de son expansion sont celles qui donnent les produits les plus diversifiés et les plus compliqués, comme l'automobile ou l'électronique. On retrouve là sous une nouvelle forme mais avec toutes les servitudes qu'il comportait pour les pays neufs, le pacte colonial, en ce sens que restent réservés aux métropoles tous les produits manufacturés évolués, et en particulier toute la fourniture de cet équipement moderne si impérativement nécessaire à l'évolution des pays africains. Il faudra beaucoup de diplomatie réciproque pour franchir ce premier écueil psychologique et prendre conscience qu'il s'agit là d'une inéluctable sujétion économique et technique.

Au-delà du handicap des seuils de production, et malgré la protection des restrictions de change ou des droits de douane,

F

d'autres difficultés se dresseront devant le développement des industries de consommation locale.

Les importateurs, en effet, n'accepteront pas de gaieté de cœur de voir ces produits locaux satisfaire à la quasi totalité de l'expansion de la demande du pays. Et pourtant, il ne s'agira le plus souvent que d'un amenuisement de leur position relative, et non d'une diminution de leur chiffre d'affaires absolu, et cela sur une portion relativement limitée du marché. Ce recul partiel sera d'ailleurs compensé par l'augmentation des ventes, corrélative à la croissance du revenu national et par conséquent de la demande, pour ceux des produits métropolitains à la fabrication desquels n'aura point encore accédé l'industrie locale. Rappel à nouveau du pacte colonial, ce fait aura plutôt tendance à favoriser l'envol des pays industriels vers la pointe du progrès technique et il devrait à ce titre entraîner l'adhésion de principe, à cette politique de substitution, des gouvernements des grandes nations, à défaut de celle de leurs commerçants ou de leurs producteurs. Les entrepreneurs privés sont en effet peu enclins à à sacrifier des avantages qu'ils estimaient définitivement acquis. C'est là un des aspects courants du problème de la décolonisation, en même temps qu'un des facteurs qui risquent de peser lourdement sur le climat psychologique dans lequel auront à évoluer dans ces pays les ressortissants étrangers.

De toutes façons, malgré ces difficultés, le développement économique de l'Afrique, l'accroissement de sa population, et l'augmentation de ses besoins individuels, y feront s'y créer progressivement de nouvelles industries de consommation, chaque région s'inscrivant à chaque instant à son niveau propre d'essor et d'équipement. On trouve d'ailleurs, à travers le monde, depuis les grandes métropoles arrivées à l'âge de l'atome et des satellites artificiels et les pays intégralement neufs, tous les degrés possibles de l'industrialisation. Ainsi, du Thibet à l'Amérique du Nord, on rencontre le Congo déjà fortement pourvu des industries de démarrage, puis l'Inde et le Brésil qui érigent leur sidérurgie, puis encore l'Afrique du Sud où l'on fabrique des pneus et du pétrole synthétique.

Ce caractère des industries de consommation des pays neufs de devoir se limiter à des produits manufacturés simples, car seuls compatibles avec les données immédiates de l'économie locale, a une incidence directe sur la définition et le volume des échanges extérieurs de ces pays. La similitude qui s'observera inéluctablement entre les modes et conditions de vie des pays neufs et des pays plus évolués, y fera utiliser, avec une intensité inverse de leur complexité, toute la gamme de la production des nations les plus industrielles. C'est là une nécessité irréversible de l'effort d'intégration des pays neufs à l'activité mondiale, nécessité qui les place dans une situation fondamentalement différente de celle qu'ont connue, au moment où leur niveau de vie était voisin de celui des actuelles régions sous-développées, les pays guides de l'activité industrielle. La consommation de ces pays guides a toujours été en effet dans l'impossibilité matérielle, et y est toujours, d'anticiper sur le niveau de leur progrès industriel propre.

Nouveau rappel des pactes coloniaux, cette consommation au-delà des produits locaux, contraindra donc les pays sous-développés à des importations importantes d'articles évolués et chers, notamment de biens d'équipement. C'est là, indépendamment de toute position idéologique, une nécessité imposée par l'organisation actuelle de l'économie mondiale. La Chine communiste elle-même, par exemple, a payé et continue de payer une bonne partie de ses produits d'équipement par des exportations de denrées alimentaires, quelquefois au prix d'un rationnement de sa population.

Dans l'économie des pays neufs, *les échanges extérieurs devront donc avoir une place relative infiniment plus considérable que celle strictement nécessaire à l'évolution, dans la prosperité, des pays industriels*, et ces pays neufs, pour assurer leur progrès dans l'indépendance, devront prendre une position exportatrice d'autant plus considérable qu'ils recherchent une vitesse d'évolution plus grande. Il est donc normal que *pour améliorer cette position exportatrice*, les pays neufs chercheront à incorporer à leurs matières premières le maximum de valeur qu'il sera possible localement d'ajouter, moyennant des transformations industrielles plus ou moins poussées.

Ces industries exportatrices devront, cependant, être compétitives sur les centres de consommation mondiaux, c'est-à-dire y offrir concurrentiellement leurs produits, à des prix incorporant le coût des transports depuis le lieu de fabrication. Or, ces industries ne commandent pas, en général, le prix des transports : elles le subissent, et s'il s'agit de produits pauvres, il peut être très supérieur à celui de la valeur départ de la marchandise.

Par exemple, dans les années 30, l'Ouest de Madagascar exportait du maïs vers la France à un prix d'environ 1.000 frs la tonne rendue ports français. Mais la valeur FOB était de 125 à 150 frs, et elle descendait en moyenne au-dessous de la moitié de ces chiffres au départ des cultures. Avec la diffusion de l'information, de tels faits ne pouvaient manquer de conduire, sur les plans psychologiques et politiques, à de dangereuses comparaisons quant à la situation relative des producteurs métropolitains et coloniaux. A un degré moindre, nous allons retrouver ces difficultés dans le domaine industriel. Sauf rares exceptions, les industries à vocation exportatrice des pays neufs ne sont pas d'une ampleur telle qu'elles puissent dominer les marchés mondiaux et y imposer leurs prix. C'est donc à la consommation que se fixeront les cours, dont les variations par suite de l'incidence du coût des transports, se reportent intégralement mais avec une ampleur relative accrue, sur les valeurs départ. Subissant les conditions du marché mondial, la ressource valorisée reste sous la menace des fluctuations des cours internationaux. Devant produire aux cours mondiaux diminués du coût des transports, la rente du site se trouve pratiquement absorbée par ces derniers même si l'on ne procède, au début, qu'à l'écrémage de la ressource (on n'a initialement exploité en Nouvelle Calédonie que les minerais à plus de 3% de nickel, alors qu'ils ne représentent qu'une faible partie des réserves locales) au risque d'hypothéquer et d'engager gravement l'avenir.

De plus, obligées, pour ces motifs, à comprimer au maximum les prix de revient départ, les industries exportatrices sont amenées à limiter au plus bas la rémunération de la main-d'œuvre, et à s'opposer en permanence à l'augmentation des salaires. Cette pression sur les salaires est d'ailleurs facilitée par la situation de l'emploi dans les pays d'Afrique noire à populations en très grande majorité rurales et vivant dans une économie de subsistance en dehors des circuits économiques et monétaires. Une partie de cette population peut donc être employée par l'industrie moyennant des salaires ou autres avantages dépassant à peine le minimum vital des pays en cause.

Ce minimum peut même être maintenu constant jusqu'à ce que l'ensemble de la population soit engagé dans les circuits économiques. On réalise ainsi une phase de développement à niveau de vie constant, ce qui cadre avec une des servitudes dites "nécessaires" des industries exportatrices. Un tel phénomène paraît avoir été caractéristique de beaucoup de pays colonisés et il n'a commencé qu' assez récemment à céder sous l'impulsion politique de l'opinion mondiale ou locale. Ce maintien à un taux constant du niveau de vie indigène constitue d'ailleurs le plus grave reproche que les nouveaux dirigeants des nouveaux états indépendants font au processus d'industrialisation du colonisateur.

Les servitudes communes à toutes les activités industrielles qui se développeront en Afrique méritent également d'être étudiées à ce stade de notre exposé. La première est que les investissements qu'elles nécessitent ainsi que certains des frais d'exploitation sont comparativement beaucoup plus élevés que dans les pays déjà industrialisés. Ce prix plus élevé des investissements tient d'abord au fait que les biens d'équipement doivent être importés et que, par conséquent, leur coût est majoré du montant des transports, à l'inverse de ce qui se passe pour la valeur départ des produits à l'exportation; de plus, ces biens d'équipement doivent souvent être adaptés presqu'unité par unité, donc à coût élevé, aux conditions de fonctionnement équatorial ou tropical, avec mise au point définitive par des monteurs spécialisés. Ce prix plus élevé tient aussi, et peut-être surtout, au fait que dans les pays sous-développés, une activité quelconque entraîne, même si elle est implantée dans les grands centres, toute une série d'installations et d'immobilisations annexes dont on n'a pas ou beaucoup moins à se préoccuper dans les métro-poles: habitat du personnel et services sociaux, création d'installations qui sont normalement, dans les régions industrialisées, des services publics (voies de communication, eau, énergie, etc.), importance plus grande des approvisionnement généraux des ateliers d'entretien et des magasins de pièces de rechange en raison des importants délais de livraison et du fait que pour certaines pièces spéciales on ne peut se fier aux possibilités du commerce local.

Ces servitudes ont, cependant, certaines conséquences indirectes bénéfiques car elles obligent les promoteurs d'activités nouvelles à étudier plus en détail l'intégration de leur affaire à la vie du pays et à éviter les excès auxquels a conduit dans l'Europe du 19ème siècle la seule considération de l'aspect capitaliste de l'entreprise. Mais ce bénéfice n'est qu'indirect et pas immédiatement perceptible.

Le résultat de ces servitudes est de majorer de 30 à 40% au moins le coût des investissements par rapport à ce qu'il est dans les pays industriels. Une telle différence est déjà un sévère handicap pour l'industrialisation de l'Afrique noire. Mais ce qui est plus grave, c'est que la rémunération de ce capital doit être prévue dans les prix de revient.

De même, le coût des produits de consommation ou d'entretien importés, pièces de rechange en particulier, et celui des spécialistes étrangers à salaires d'expatriation élevés accroissent dans des proportions très considérables les frais d'exploitation, sans grand profit pour le multiplicateur local d'activité.

En ce qui concerne ce dernier point, il faut d'ailleurs remarquer que du fait de la rupture de l'intégration économique et financière des nouveaux états avec leur ancienne métropole, *le facteur de multiplication* ne peut plus être considéré comme par le passé par rapport à l'ensemble intégré, mais il doit être estimé séparément pour chacune des économies intéressées.

Or, avant la conquête coloniale, ces régions africaines ne connaissaient ni circulation monétaire ni capital local, et le capital indigène n'a pas pu depuis s'y créer à un niveau suffisant, surtout dans les pays à colonisation paternaliste. L'argent nécessaire à l'équipement industriel ne peut encore et pour longtemps être qu'étranger, l'intervention de l'état, avec tout ce que l'Europe lui attache de signification politique, étant la seule forme de participation locale possible. Or qui dit investissements étrangers dit transfert obligatoire (au moins à terme) de leur rémunération pour qu'ils puissent continuer à venir à la fois alimenter l'expansion et assurer l'équilibre de la balance des comptes ainsi que la stabilité monétaire.

De ce point de vue, la situation des pays neufs est structurellement différente de celle des régions industrielles où les investissements étrangers se font normalement sur une base de réciprocité, et où il n'y a pratiquement pas d'écart sensible du multiplicateur suivant l'origine des investissements.

Cette nécessité du financement extérieur conduit à considérer, par exemple, que tout se passe comme si l'énergie des aménagements hydroélectriques réalisés était importée à 60 ou 80% de sa valeur suivant les cas. Il ne faut donc pas s'étonner qu'un pareil fait rende fort attractives non dans l'immédiat mais à terme, après un début suffisant de formation de capital autochtone, les procédures de nationalisation. Ces procédures ont d'ailleurs pour elles, et dès maintenant, un second attrait, car la nationalisation permet de disposer en toute souveraineté des tarifs des services publics.

De même, les dirigeants des nouveaux états indépendants accepteront malaisément les contraintes résultant du fait que le capital étranger qui viendra s'investir voudra l'être dans des emplois spécifiques (ce qui sera encore plus mal admis pour les capitaux publics, et surtout pour ceux de l'ancienne nation colonisatrice), et qu'ensuite la réduction du multiplicateur local due au transfert de la rémunération des capitaux ne permettra pas d'arriver assez vite à la formation de capital autochtone. D'où risque de dangereuses manifestations d'impatience.

Cette réduction du multiplicateur, rapport au niveau correspondant à la même activité dans un pays évolué, est un fait dont les autorités responsables des plans devront tirer les conséquences. Il ne suffira plus d'étudier dans le détail la rentabilité d'une industrie nouvelle. Il faudra s'attacher aussi, et peut-être surtout, à calculer et à mettre en évidence *l'incidence des divers facteurs sur le multiplicateur local.*

En Afrique noire, pour toute activité industrielle nouvelle, cette incidence sur le multiplicateur local sera le plus souvent presque nulle en ce qui concerne le capital investi, très limitée pour tous les produits importés dont en particulier les pièces de rechange, faible pour la main-d'œuvre puisque cadres et maîtrise vireront à l'étranger leurs excédents et que les ouvriers et manœuvres indigènes devront, pour compenser d'autres servitudes, se contenter de bas salaires compte tenu du niveau d'ensemble du revenu national.

Ne joueront à plein, et c'est la raison pour laquelle il faut encourager l'installation d'activités industrielles nouvelles, que les appels de ces industries aux services locaux ainsi que le produit des impôts et taxes qu'il sera possible de prélever.

En un sens, c'est donc le sous-développement lui-même qui est la cause du manque actuel d'efficience de l'industrialisation. En particulier, la limitation des marchés intérieurs dont la raison essentielle est l'insuffisance du revenu des habitants, oppose dans de nombreux cas aux industries de consommation locale la barrière des seuils techniques. On retrouve là, à une échelle réduite, les considérations qui ont conduit l'Europe des Six, puis d'autres pays, vers le Marché Commun. De même, l'absence de capital autochtone qui rend nécessaire l'appel aux investissements étrangers et le transfert à terme de sa rémunération, le manque d'indigènes de formation suffisante pour occuper les postes à hauts salaires de direction et de maîtrise, le recours obligatoire aux fournisseurs étrangers pour tout bien d'équipement et même pour toute matière consommable un peu élaborée diminuent dans une proportion très considérable le multiplicateur local des activités industrielles et ce que ces dernières peuvent induire d'expansion.

Il n'en reste pas moins que les nations du monde occidental, si elles veulent sauvegarder leurs intérêts acquis et leur prestige moral, doivent apporter leur concours financier et technique à cette industrialisation.

Mais si l'on ne veut point connaître trop de déchets, et c'est indispensable pour l'avenir des pays neufs, il ne faudra procéder à cette industrialisation qu'à travers un minimum de planification tenant compte des limites qui s'imposent: limites humaines en main d'œuvre, cadres et maîtrise, limites des capitaux disponibles, limites des débouchés, etc.

Il faudra aussi faire que cette industrialisation soit intégrée *dans un développement d'ensemble* harmonisé assurant en profondeur l'expansion rationnelle de toutes les activités de la collectivité en cause et le mieux-être de tous ses participants. On accélérera ainsi la cadence possible d'implantation de nouvelles activités industrielles, par le recul des limites aux investissements, et l'on augmentera leur efficience et leur aptitude à entraîner des développements induits, par l'accroissement du recours aux moyens locaux. On tendra donc à amorcer de cette façon une réaction en chaîne vers l'expansion et vers le progrès.

Il n'y a pas de solution au sous-développement en dehors d'une action généralisée et cohérente sur tous les éléments d'une économie encore dans la première enfance. Il faut donc procéder, sans exclusive ni idée préconçue, à la mobilisation générale de toutes les ressources du pays, des plus modestes jusqu'à celles révélées par les projets les plus vastes.

Cette action tiendra compte en particulier du fait que, dans les pays de l'Afrique noire, comme dans l'Europe d'il y a quelques siècles, la quasi totalité de la population est rurale. Cette population se trouve donc à la fois dans un état de sous-emploi caractérisé, ce qui laisse une somme importante de travail disponible pour le développement du pays, et dans une économie de subsistance, presque complétement isolée des circuits économiques et monétaires.

L'analyse qui précède conduit donc à dépasser le seul aspect industriel du problème. Sur le plan des principes, les éléments essentiels de la solution du sous-développement semblent alors les suivants:

—réaliser tout d'abord un important développement de la production nationale, d'une part, pour augmenter le niveau de vie des habitants de façon à bien asseoir le marché des productions locales, d'autre part, pour rendre disponibles pour l'exportation, au-delà de la consommation interne, de larges excédents de produits locaux;

—obtenir surtout cet accroissement en mettant en œuvre celles des activités nouvelles qui offrent les meilleures perspectives de développement ultérieur. Ceci se traduira par la sélection d'entreprises qui ont le multiplicateur interne le plus élevé et qui contribuent le plus aux exportations. Le volume de ces dernières devra d'ailleurs être d'autant plus grand que la vitesse d'équipement recherchée sera plus grande.

La recherche de débouchés stables, tant pour les besoins que pour les prix, jouera aussi un grand rôle. Il pourra donc être opportun de s'engager à long terme dans la voie d'échange de services réciproques avec des pays à économie complémentaire. C'est dans cette optique que se situent des conceptions comme le Commonwealth, l'ex-Communauté française, l'Association dans le cadre du Marché Commun, et les espoirs d'une Eurafrique.

Cette simple énumération suffit à définir l'ampleur du problème à résoudre. Elle situe l'importance, dans cette solution, de l'aide étrangère, indépendamment de toute idéologie, et des ressources locales disponibles dont la mobilisation générale s'impose.

La situation de départ des pays sous-développés est d'ailleurs plus favorable que ne l'était celle des pays d'Europe à l'aube de l'essor des techniques. La seule source initiale de richesses résidait alors dans l'accumulation modeste et patiente du travail de tous. Ce travail est maintenant inséparable de tout un acquis technique (miraculeux fruit d'une laborieuse gestation) et il n'est donc plus qu'une de ressources principales à la disposition de ces pays. C'est aux pays neufs à faire appel à la technique pour faire fructifier le propre travail de leurs populations. Il importe pour ces pays de déterminer exactement ce qu'ils peuvent en attendre compte tenu de leurs propres ressources, et en particulier de leurs hommes.

5

DYNAMIC PLANNING OF INDUSTRIAL GROWTH IN EMERGING COUNTRIES

A. T. MATERNA AND R. D. ARCHIBALD

CPM Systems Inc., Construction Project Management,
Encino, California,

PREFACE

THE high standard of living of the Western world has been based on a free-enterprise economy. Although we believe that this is the best economic system, we must realize that it has been evolved from an agricultural economy into an industrial economy over a period of more than a hundred years. The underdeveloped countries are understandably impatient to raise their standard of living by taking advantage of available technology and developing their resources as fast as possible. This desire leads invariably to centralized planning and control of the economy. Large amounts of money, mainly in the form of foreign aid, are generally at the disposal of this centralized planning function.

The problem of making the most effective use of the available funds can be resolved through the application of operations research techniques and electronic data processing.

In this paper an approach is described for allocation of funds and manpower, and scheduling of projects so that the economy can be developed in the proper sequence of selective development of major industrial sectors.

INTRODUCTION

During the past 15 years, financial assistance to emerging countries has amounted to more than $70 billion in foreign aid and investment. This year another $7 billion will be invested for the economic development of these areas. If these large sums of money are to be spent efficiently to provide the most rapid growth, considerable emphasis must be placed on planning and co-ordination. Sophisticated techniques for planning and monitoring the progress of multi-million-dollar projects have become accepted in managing industrial and military programs in the United States. Similar techniques are necessary for the planning and control of economic development programs in the new nations of the world.

The purpose of this paper is to demonstrate how an advanced management technique now in use in the United States can be used beneficially in managing the industrial growth of emerging countries. For any large project, a plan must be formulated, recorded, and all management levels made aware of its details. The essential problem with traditional planning methods, when applied to rapidly changing situations, is the inflexibility of the planning system. If changes are not rapidly reflected in the complete set of plans, then confusion, unco-ordinated action, and waste will inevitably result. Without a dynamic planning system, plans soon become obsolete and often an obstacle to progress. Very soon, all concerned lose confidence in official plans, and decisions are based on guesswork.

The planning of industrial growth is concerned with the interdependence of the basic industries such as mining, power, steel, transportation, and communications. In some cases the timing of the development of one industrial sector has been out of phase with the other sectors. For example, in northern India, a mine and a foundry were completed 3 years before a connecting railroad. As a result, several hundred thousand dollars had to be spent on overhauling rusty equipment before the mine and foundry could be put into operation. A dynamic system for planning the allocation of resources and evaluating progress must take into account these interrelationships. A number of studies have been made and mathematical models formulated for this kind of problem. Several algorithms are available to optimize resource allocation. However, most of the models are static rather than dynamic. Furthermore, these models are, in general, too sophisticated for the information available. In our opinion, the first step toward better management and coordination of industrial growth is not in the formulation of elegant mathematical solutions, but the improvement of the quality and timeliness of the information provided to management for planning.

The information system described in this paper has several new features. In addition to the scheduling technique now mandatory in many U.S. military projects, it includes cost and manpower planning and review. Further, it recognizes the need for more than one level of management reporting. This system has been developed from actual experience to meet management needs for better understanding of the impact of current progress on future plans. Such a system would accomplish not only better planning, but it would help to speed up the industrialization so vital to its growth. Further, it would assist in better utilization of its scarce, skilled manpower and would bring the shortage of skills to the planners' attention far in advance so that vocational training could be started. The subsequent result of balanced industrial development program would attract additional capital to continue further industrial expansion. It should be pointed out that such a system should not give the government monopoly in planning, but should only monitor the progress of the expansion based on private enterprise needs.

Although it is fully recognized that the limiting factor in all underdeveloped countries are social or political rather than technological, undoubtedly the design of a progress reporting and management system for projects is a task which should pay rich dividends in the planning of industrial growth in emerging countries. For the purpose of this paper, we are going to confine ourselves to the problem of project management, and leave the questions of social and political problems to others who might be better qualified.

It is our belief that the project management should be of interest to such organizations as the United States Agency for International Development, or the Organization for Economic Co-operation and Development which handle a multitude of large projects and programs.

EVOLUTION OF THE NETWORK PLAN CONCEPT

The early general work which started the evolution of the network-based system of today was primarily reported by Salveson almost 10 years ago. The evolution of the arrow diagram concept or the network plan, which is the backbone of both the critical path method and PERT, is the fundamentally important step forward which has enabled rapid progress in the development of better management information and control systems. Figure 1 illustrates the steps leading from the familiar Gantt bar chart to the network plan. The Gantt chart is a number of bars plotted against a time scale, each representing the beginning, duration, and end of some jobs competing for the same labor pool or facilities. Over the years, this chart proved to be extremely useful in production scheduling. However, for large and complex undertakings, it has serious deficiencies. These include (1) the lack of recognition of the interdependencies which exist between the efforts represented by the bars, (2) the static nature of this diagram and its difficulty to reflect the dynamic nature of changing plans, (3) the lack of ability to reflect uncertainties or tolerances in time estimates, and (4) the difficulty of summarizing the critical problems in a meaningful management report.

The first step in preparing a network plan is the establishment of a careful definition of events and activities. These are defined as follows:

Event: A meaningful specified accomplishment (physical or intellectual) in the program plan, recognizable as a particular instant in time. Events do not consume time or resources, and are normally represented in the network by circles or rectangles.

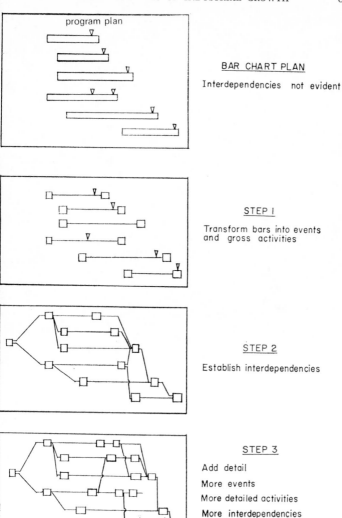

program plan

BAR CHART PLAN

Interdependencies not evident

STEP 1

Transform bars into events
and gross activities

STEP 2

Establish interdependencies

STEP 3

Add detail
More events
More detailed activities
More interdependencies

FIG. 1. *Evolution of the network plan concept.*

Activity: An activity is a time-consuming element in the execution of a task. It is represented on a network or flow chart by an arrow. An event is separated from another event by an activity. An activity cannot be started until its preceding event has been accomplished. A succeeding event to an activity cannot be accomplished until the activity is complete.

Good activity definition is necessary so that the best possible time and resource estimates can be obtained, and later on it helps in defining the actual progress which has been made in the total program.

Step two relates the interdependencies between the major elements of effort in a given plan. These may be called "constraints" or "dummy activities". Preferred practice is to define these in such a way that no resources are expended on constraining activities since they usually represent transfer of information or hardware from one organization to another.

The third major step in developing the network plan consists of adding more events which can be used to correlate the beginning and end of the activities. At this time it is also possible to add the interdependencies or interfaces of the various activities. Basically, a network plan is defined as a graphic portrayal of a plan showing the time dependencies and chronological sequence of events and activities leading to a given end objective.

HUGHES–PERT MANAGEMENT INFORMATION SYSTEM

Hughes–PERT is an extension of the basic PERT/Time system under which a development project is first broken down into several major projects which make up the total program, and then into functional tasks which could be assigned to first line operating supervisors. These work tasks are then divided into more detailed activities and plotted on a conventional PERT network to establish the interdependencies of the activities and the sequence in which the work will be performed. The sequence in which the activities are planned to be performed creates various "paths" from the beginning to the end of the project network. The total time of each path is the sum of all activities along this path. The critical path is the longest time path to the end of the network as it determines the final completion of the program.

The extension of the basic PERT system by integrating cost and manpower with the common time oriented network not only permits more accurate measurement of progress but also enables managers to appraise more realistically the consequences of alternative courses of action.

SUMMARY OF THE SYSTEM CAPABILITIES

Before proceeding with a detailed explanation of the mechanics and semantics of the Hughes–PERT system, it will be helpful to list briefly the major capabilities which are made possible by using the proper system.

Time Schedule Analysis. A simple but very useful time schedule analysis method enables realistic evaluation of the plan portrayed by the network and comparison to the time schedule.

Progress Evaluation. As the plan is put into operation, the network is updated through reporting of current activity completions and by revision to show any changes in the future plan. Analysis of the updated network can quickly reveal the effect if these changes and future problem areas.

Mechanized Analysis of Plans. The system has been designed and developed for electronic data processing to take advantage of the computer capabilities to handle large and tedious information processing.

Integration of Plans. The network provides means for numerous and diverse elements of a plan to be brought together and integrated into one large program or regional planning structure.

Planning Manpower, Funding, and Other Resources. The system has been designed to handle, in addition to the time scheduling, planning of manpower, cost and facilities. By successive iterations,

G

the system can provide information by simulating the proposed decisions and their effect on the overall program.

THE HUGHES–PERT SYSTEM

Hughes–PERT has several important features. First of all, it integrates the three basic elements in management; time, manpower, and costs. Further, it recognizes the need for more than one level of management reporting. This system, which has been developed from actual experience, meets management needs for better understanding of the impact of current progress on future plans. Although the concepts in PERT are simple and readily understandable, the actual preparation of a valid, useful network plan is a difficult job.

Objective of the Hughes–PERT System

The basic objective of the Hughes–PERT system is to lock together the jobs (or activities) to be done with the related schedule, manpower, and dollar information pertaining to the accomplishment of a project-type effort. The network plan, which is a realistic, understandable model of the project, provides the framework of the system, enabling these elements of planning information to be linked together, and also correlating the actual expenditures of time, labor, and funds against the plan. The Hughes–PERT system prepares and presents this integrated information to managers for their review, to assist in their making the decisions which control the project.

Hughes–PERT System Description

The Hughes–PERT Information System is based on a multi-level Work Breakdown Structure which provides the overall program or project definition necessary for meaningful summarization of time, cost, and manpower information. The establishment of this structure with related network plans is shown in Fig. 2. Steps 1-A through E, 2, 3, and 4 follow the operational steps in the system.

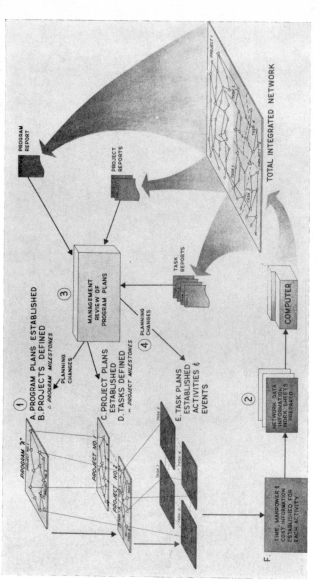

Fig. 2. *Establishment of program network plans. Hughes-PERT System*

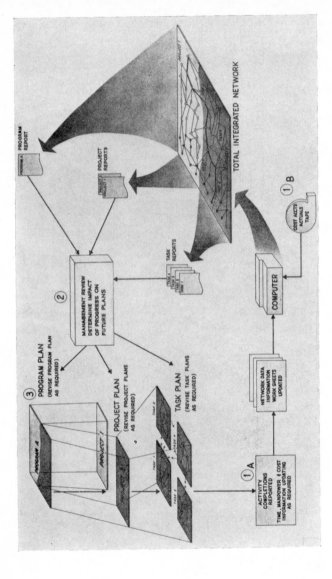

Fig. 3. *Up-Dating Cycle. Hughes-PERT System*

It is most important, during the definition of the Work Breakdown Structure (step 1), to identify interface events, or those events signaling the transfer of responsibility from one part of the work breakdown to another. These interface events, together with important milestone events, are carried down to the task level and form the skeleton of the detailed activity/event networks. After the detailed networks have been prepared, they are then integrated on the computer through the common interface events into the total network as shown.

Reports are automatically prepared by summarizing the proper data contained in the total integrated network at each of the three levels in the Work Breakdown Structure. Visibility is thus provided at these levels of summary appropriate to the scope of responsibility of each supervisor or manager. On small efforts, only one or two levels of summary need be used.

Management review of the program planning information thus provided determines whether the plans are acceptable in terms of time schedule, estimated costs, and estimated manpower requirements over time. The resulting decisions are reflected as planning changes at the proper level in the Work Breakdown Structure.

The System Up-Dating Cycle is illustrated in Fig. 3, in which steps 1-A and B, 2, and 3 follow the sequence of operations. Step 1-A consists of the reporting of completions and revision of estimated data, and step 1-B, the feeding in of the cost expenditure information from the cost accounting system. In step 2, management review of the updated reports determine the impact of the time/cost/labor progress on the remainder of the plan, and step 3 consists of changing the plan as required to execute the resulting management decisions.

Output Reports of the Hughes–PERT System

Once a good Work Breakdown Structure has been established, and the detailed networks have been proved out, summarized results of several kinds can be obtained by the computer. The major categories of summary are:

1. Work Breakdown Structure.
2. Contract (Fiscal) Structure.
3. Organizational Structure.
4. Produce End-use (or Mission) Structure.

These are made possible by the cross-referencing of activities (or groups of activities) in the four categories listed. (It is not mandatory, of course, to use all four designations, at all times, but only if a specific summary type is desired.) Each activity is identified with a Task, which allows it to be summed through the Work Breakdown Structure; it is also identified to a contract, through the charge number to which it is assigned; further, it is identified to a performing organization; and, finally, it can be given a code to identify it to a major end use.

Hughes–PERT Management Reports

The Hughes–PERT Management Reports illustrated in this section make available in the written and diagrammatic form the time schedule manpower and cost data that the contractor and government management needs to plan and monitor their projects. These reports provide at each level of management the following information:

1. The latest plans at each level.
2. Time and cost performance to date in relation to the plan.
3. Manpower utilization and projection for completion of the project objectives.
4. Time and cost performance against budget.

The Hughes–PERT reports are summarized for each level of management, thereby relieving a manager of the need to review detailed information. For subordinate levels, however, this detailed information is available to him without additional processing should a need for such additional information arise. All Hughes–PERT reports use the same format although they deal with different levels of management. Hughes–PERT reports are prepared to coincide with normal accounting procedures. However, the management may use them more frequently if desired.

Current Hughes–PERT Output Reports

The currently available output reports in the Hughes–PERT system relate to the Work Breakdown Structure. These consist of graphic charts and tabular reports, as follows:

1. Time vs. Dollars (Fig. 4)

    Contents: Costs incurred to date, estimate to complete, and budget.

    Provided for: Tasks, Projects, and Program (the figures illustrate Task level summaries).

2. Time vs. Labor (Fig. 5)

    Contents: Labor expended to date, estimate to complete, and budget.

    Provided for: Tasks, Projects, and Program.

3. Time vs. Manloading (Fig. 6)

    Contents: Direct manpower charged per week, planned manpower per week, and equivalent number of people current charging by organization.

    Provided for: Tasks, Projects, and Program.

4. Milestone Chart (Fig. 7)

    Contents: Milestone event expected or actual, scheduled, and latest allowable completion dates, probability of meeting schedule.

    Provided for: Tasks, Projects, and Program Milestones.

5. Bar Charts (Fig. 8)

    Contents: Duration of effort, start and completion dates, latest allowable completion dates.

    Provided for: Activities, Tasks, Projects, and Program.

HUGHES -- OUTLOOK CHART -- PERT -- TIME VS DOLLARS

TASK

RUN DATE 02 MAY 62	CUST NO AND NAME 001 NASA -GODDARD SPACE FLIGHT CENTER
TIME DATA AS OF 31 MAR 62	PROG NO AND DES 0011
COST DATA AS OF 01 APR 62	PROJ NO AND DES 00111 PROJECT
RESP ORG FOR PROG 22-80-	PREPARED BY CELLI / GRICE
SCOPE OF NETWORK - PROGRAM	

RUN TYPE UD
RUN ID 000002
END EVENT 1318

TASK NO 02 DOCUMENTATION
CONTR NASA
HAC REF GLA 1326 C/A 927
RESP ORG 22-80-

WEEK IN YEAR
1961 1962

	TIME WEEKS	DOLLARS X1,000
E EST TOTAL	58	109
B BUDGETED	59	97
X TO-DATE	32	70
REMAINDER	27	27
* EST TO COMPLETE	26	39
PREDICTED BALANCE	1	-11

1.0 = $ 109,000.

LEGEND - ACTUAL XXXX ESTIMATE .....

RUN DATE   C2 MAY 62   CUST NO AND NAME 001   NASA -GODDARD SPACE FLIGHT CENTER   RUN TYPE   UD
TIME DATA AS OF 31 MAR 62   PRG NO AND DES 0011   RUN ID 000002
COST DATA AS OF 01 APR 62   PROJ NO AND DES 0011   PROJECT   END EVENT   1318
RESP ORG FOR PROG 22-80-   PREPARED BY CELLI / CRICE
SCOPE OF NETWORK - PROGRAM

TASK NO 02 DOCUMENTATION
CONTR   NASA
HAC REF   GLA 1326 C/A 927
RESP ORG 22-80-

	TIME WEEKS	LABOR MANWEEKS
E EST TOTAL	58	186 = 1.00 =
B BUDGETED	59	176
X TO-DATE	32	93
REMAINDER	27	83
• EST TO COMPLETE	26	94
PREDICTED BALANCE	1	-9

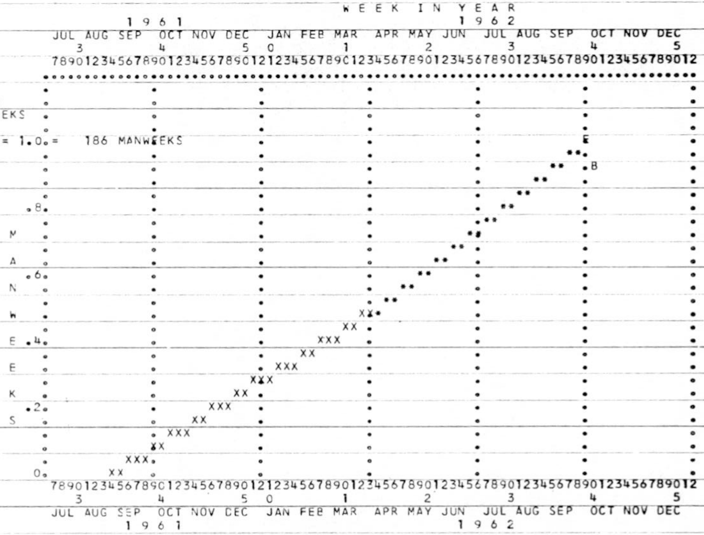

186 MANWEEKS

LEGEND - ACTUAL XXXX   ESTIMATE ....

FIG. 5

HUGHES -- PERT

TASK MANPOWER CHART

TASK   NC 02   DOCUMENTATION
CONTR   GLA 1326   C/A 927   NASA
FAC REF
RESP ORG   22-80-

WEEK IN YEAR
1962

MAXIMUM NO PEOPLE PLANNED =   4 = 1.0.

ORGANIZATIONS CURRENTLY CHARGING

ORGAN	NO PEOPLE
22-80-	3

P E O P L E   C H A R G E D   C U R R E N T L Y

1.0.
.8.
.6.
.4.
.2.
0.

LEGEND - ACTUAL XXXX   ESTIMATE ••••

MILESTONE CHART

RUN DATE   C2 MAY 62   CUST ID AND NAME 001   NASA -GODDARD SPACE FLIGHT CENTER
TIME DATA AS OF   31 MAR 62   PROG NO AND DES 0011   RUN TYPE   UD
COST DATA AS OF   01 APR 62   PROG NO AND DES 0011   RUN ID   000002
RESP ORG FOR PROG 22-90-   PREPARED BY CELLI / CRICE   PROJECT   END EVENT   1318
SCOPE OF NETWORK - PROGRAM

TASK   NC 02 DOCUMENTATION
  CONTR   NASA
  HAC REF   GLA 1328 C/A 927
  RESP ORG 22-80-

EVENT DESCRIPTION
  RESP ORG

                                                    W E E K   I N   Y E A R
                        1 9 6 1   1 9 6 2
        JUL AUG SEP OCT NOV DEC JAN FEB MAR APR MAY JUN JUL AUG SEP OCT NOV DEC
          3   4   5   0   1   2   3   4   5
        7890123456789012345678901234567890123456789012345678901234567890123456789012

COMPLETE DOCUMENTATION   Expected Completion.   P
1241   •E
  -    -   •L   •• Latest allowable.

                        Actual Completion.
START   DOCUMENTATION   •A   •   P
1215   21 AUG 61   •L   •

DOCUMENTATION THRU 3-31-62   •A
1223   31 MAR 62   •L   7890123456789012345678901234567890123456789012   P

LEGEND: PM - PROJECT MILESTONE   MM - PROGRAM MILESTONE

                                                                              P ← Planned or
                                                                                 Scheduled
                                                                                 (No date enter
                                                                                  in this task)

HUGHES -- PERT

ACTIVITY BAR CHART

```
RUN DATE            02 MAY 62     CUST NO AND NAME 001   NASA -GODDARD SPACE FLIGHT CENTER          RUN TYPE     UD
TIME DATA AS OF     31 MAR 62     PROG NO AND DES  0011                                              RUN ID  000002
COST DATA AS OF     01 APR 62     PROJ NO AND DES  00111          PROJECT                           END EVENT    1318
RESP ORG FOR PROG 22-80-          PREPARED BY CELLI / GRICE
SCOPE OF NETWORK - PROGRAM

 TASK    NO 02  DOCUMENTATION
   CONTR                         NASA
   HAC REF        GLA 1326  C/A 927
   RESP ORG  22-80-
                                                                     W E E K   I N   Y E A R
                                      1 9 6 1                               1 9 6 2
                                JUL AUG SEP  OCT NOV DEC  JAN FEB MAR  APR MAY JUN  JUL AUG SEP  OCT NOV DEC
  ACTIVITY DESCRIPTION            3           4          5  0          1            2            3            4           5
  ACTI NO  RESP ORG             789012345678901234567890121234567890123456789012345678901234567890123456789012
    PEN        SEN

  DOCUMENTATION
           22-80-
   1223       1241   EXP COMPL 30 SEP 62.                              ..........................L

  DOCUMENTATION
           22-80-                XXXXXXX
   1000       1215   ACT COMPL 21 AUG 61.       L

  DOCUMENTATION
           22-80-                    XXXXXXXXXXXXXXXXXXXXXXXXXXXXXXXX
   1215       1223   ACT COMPL 31 MAR 62.                           L

  SUST ENG COSTS
           22-80-                    XXXXXXXXXXXXXXXXXXXXXXXXXXXXXXXX..........................
   1241       1331   EXP COMPL 30 SEP 62.                                                       L

 TASK    02     OVER-ALL             XXXXXXXXXXXXXXXXXXXXXXXXXXXXXXXX..........................
   1000       1331   EXP COMPL 30 SEP 62.                                                       L
                                789012345678901234567890121234567890123456789012345678901234567890123456789012
```

RUN DATE 02 MAY 62   COST NO AND NAME 001   NASA -GODDARD SPACE FLIGHT CENTER   RUN TYPE UD
TIME DATA AS OF 31 MAR 62   PROG NO AND DES 0011   RUN ID 000002
COST DATA AS OF 01 APR 62   PKGJ NO AND DES 0011   END EVENT 1318
RESP ORG FOR PROG 22-80-   PREPARED BY CELLI / GRICE   PROJECT
SCOPE OF NETWORK - PROGRAM

TASK NO 02 DOCUMENTATION
   HDC REF   GLA 1326 C/A 927   NASA
   RESP ORG 22-80-

ACTIVITY DESCRIPTION		E S T I M A T E D -- A C T U A L C O S T S									PROGRESS RATIO		U N I T S	
ACTI NO RESP ORG		C		L A B O R		(×$1,000) MAT / OTH		TOTAL			PLAN	ACT-
PEN	SEN	N	EST	ACT	EST	ACT	COM MIT	EST	ACT	BOGT	T/C.		NED	UAL

THE FOLLOWING ACTIVITIES ALL HAVE CHRG NO-1326 9270201

DOCUMENTATION
   22-80-
   1223   1241   *   33   44   7   25   40   09
DOCUMENTATION
   22-80-
   1000   1215   *   100/
DOCUMENTATION
   22-80-
   1215   1223   *   100/
                       SUB-TOTALS   *   44   25   40   09   54/100

SUST ENG COSTS
   22-80-
   1241   1331   *
TASK   C2   TOTALS   33   44   7   25   40   59   97   54/173   E
   1000   1331   INDIRECT AMOUNTS   33   22

                                                ↑
                                    % Est. time expended / % Est. cost expended

FIG. 9

```
RUN DATE       02 MAY 62      COST NO AND NAME  001   NASA -GODDARD SPACE FLIGHT CENTER        RUN TYPE   UD
TIME DATA AS OF  31 MAR 62    PROG NO AND DES   0011                                          RUN ID  000002
COST DATA AS OF  22 APR 62    PROJ NO AND DES   0011           PROJECT                        END EVENT   1318
RESP ORG FOR PROG  22-8C-     PREPARED BY CELLI / CRICE
SCOPE OF NETWORK - PROGRAM
```

```
TASK  NO C2  DOCUMENTATION
    CONTR REF                    NASA
    HDC REF      GLA 1326   C/A 927
    RESP ORG  22-8C-
```

```
                                      C
ACTIVITY DESCRIPTION                  H   START  DATES       C O M P L E T I O N        D A T E S   SLACK   PROB
ACTI NO RESP ORG                      N                                                             WEEKS   MEET
     PEN     SEN                      G   EXPECT/ACTUAL   EXPECTED   LATEST   PLANNED   ACTUAL               PLAN
```

```
DOCUMENTATION
     22-8C-                             31 MAR 62 E     30 SEP 62   02 OCT 62                        + .3
1223           1241
```

```
DOCUMENTATION
     22-8C-                             21 AUG 61 E                 23 AUG 61             21 AUG 61   + .3
1000           1215
```

```
DOCUMENTATION
     22-8C-                             31 MAR 62 E                 02 APR 62             31 MAR 62   + .3
1215           1223
```

```
SUST ENG COSTS
     22-8C-                             30 SEP 62       30 SEP 62   02 OCT 62  01 OCT 62              + .3    .99
1241           1331
```

```
TASK  C2    SUMMARY
1000           1331                     21 AUG 61 E     30 SEP 62   02 OCT 62  01 OCT 62              + .3    .99
```

6. Cost Outlook Report (Fig. 9)

Contents: Estimated, actual, and budgeted (allocated) costs, Time/Cost Progress Ratio (per cent of estimated time expended/per cent of estimated cost expended), exception flag (calling attention to conditions which violate given rules), and planned and actual units (which are as defined by the user: black boxes, drawings, tests, etc.).

Provided for: Activities, Tasks, Projects, and Program.

7. Time Outlook Report (Fig. 10)

Contents: Expected or actual start dates; expected, latest allowable, planned (scheduled) or actual completion dates; slack; probability of meeting the planned date.

Provided for: Activities, Tasks, Projects, and Program.

NOTE: The reports presented in this paper are illustrations of Hughes–PERT application to a military program. However, it should be noted that the data that appear in the reports are for illustration only and do not indicate the current status of any real project.

Hughes–PERT Management Information System collects, synthesizes, transmits and displays information. The flow is from a primary source of information to the manager. The subsequent application of judgment and additional knowledge by the manager, his decision actions and the following transmittal of the decision to the affected persons or operations are not considered to be within the scope of the definition of management information systems. Hughes–PERT was designed to provide managers at various levels with the information each one needs to make decisions related to his responsibilities.

Most effective use of the result produced by the Hughes–PERT system requires proper utilization of summary reports and correlation and display of these results. Well-designed display boards and panels on which current computer outputs can be mounted and suitable graphic interpretations are vitally important. Many companies are turning to the control room concept in which summaries of all major projects or programs are displayed. Top management can be appraised of the status and outlook of all major efforts in a very short time and communication regarding correction of problem areas is made easier.

INPUT REQUIREMENTS OF THE HUGHES–PERT SYSTEM

Time information is input to the system at the activity level, in normal PERT/Time fashion for both estimates and actual completions.

Manpower estimates are best entered at the activity level as direct manloading (average number of people to be assigned to the activity); however, these estimates can be entered by activity groups (sub-tasks or Tasks) and/or by manhours instead of number of men. Labor cost estimates are calculated on the computer by multiplying the activity time estimate by the number of men, then by a labor cost rate for the performing organization. Overhead rates are applied by the computer if desired.

Non-labor cost estimates are best entered at the activity level in hundreds of dollars, but can be entered by activity group or Task, if desired.

Labor and non-labor expenditures are obtained directly from tape records used in the cost accounting system without manual transcription of the data. The "charging level" is flexible and may be either at the activity level (i.e. a single charge number for a given activity), or by activity groups (one charge number for any number of related activities). The computer automatically prepares sub-totals in the latter case.

Machine input requirements. Two 80-column punched cards are required for each activity in the network, as illustrated in Fig. 11. In addition, description and budgeting information must be entered one time for Tasks, Projects, and the Program, and in the event Milestone Charts are desired, one card per milestone is necessary.

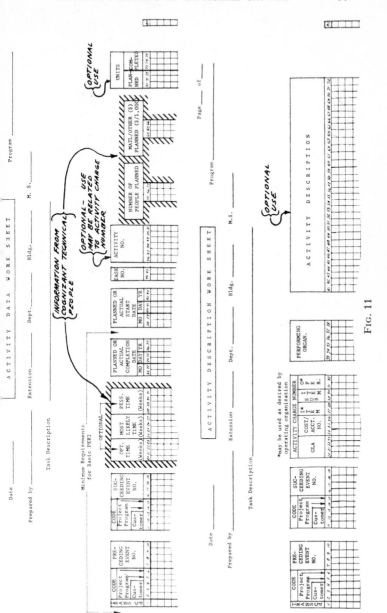

FIG. 11

H

OPERATION OF THE HUGHES–PERT MANAGEMENT INFORMATION SYSTEM

The flow of information through the system is shown in Fig. 12, which illustrates the three levels of system operations:

Program Management
  Review of Planning Documents;
  Decision; and
  Ordering changes.

Program Planning
  Preparing graphic network plans and estimates;
  Controlling preparation; and
  Distribution of Planning Documents.

Computer Center
  Preparing input data in machine format;
  Editing and merging all input data on tape; and
  Preparing computer analysis of the plans and printing out the Planning Documents are requested by the Program Planning Unit.

The information system described, when used for planning industrial growth in emerging countries, would assist the Program Management function. Program Planning would be decentralized to the operating project level. This function would assist the project managers in their task of budgeting and control. Machine processing of the information is a service function and as such could be carried on in a different geographical location from the Program Management.

MULTI-PROJECT MANAGEMENT

When separate organizations (different companies, different departments within companies, or various government agencies) are working on different parts of the same total effort, each organizational element will lay out its plan for its limited part of the overall program. Initially, a broad overall plan should have been established to correlate the various parts and provide a starting-point from which

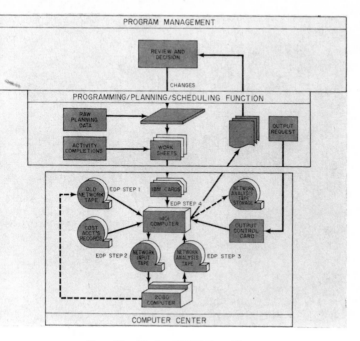

FIG. 12.   *Hughes-PERT Data Flow*

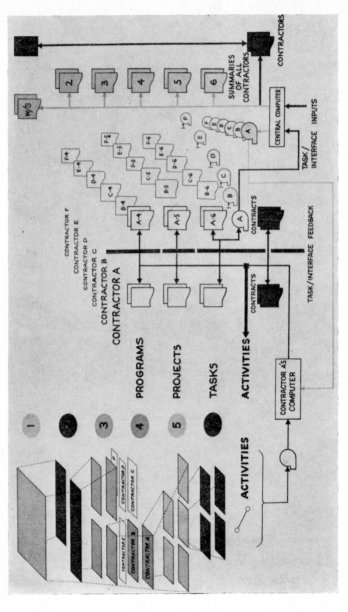

FIG. 13. *Integrated PERT system*

each organization can develop its plan; but after each detailed plan has been prepared, it is essential that they be tied together or integrated in order to determine the total effect of the interactions and interdependencies. The network plan provides a simple and effective technique for accomplishing this through interface events. Each separate portion of a plan may be sound and valid by itself, and yet when all elements are integrated, serious conflicts are revealed.

The term "network integration" is now commonly accepted to mean the linking together of previously separate activity-event network plans by common or interface events. An interface event has been previously defined as the point at which responsibility for a given action changes hands. Integration is thus a meshing of plans by joining at well-identified points, denoting the transfer of responsibility.

The importance of systematic planning becomes evident when attempting to integrate networks. Proper breakdown of the overall program elements and identification of milestones and interface for each element at each level of management interests are essential. Careful study to determine the number and scope of networks is necessary with the objective of minimizing the total number of individual networks, since this simplifies the analysis and integration problem.

Serious consideration should be given to forcibly limiting the size of the total network to the maximum which can be handled by the available computer program. In a large computer such as the IBM 7090 this limit is usually around 5000 activities, which should be ample even for very large efforts. Manual reduction of large networks using judgment to combine and remove activities has been found to be an effective way to improve the analysis workload.

There will be major programs which will have total network exceeding current computer limits. However, even if unlimited computer programs were generally available, experience with fairly large networks to date has shown that handling of such vast amounts of input data becomes impractical, especially if the network is dynamic and rapidly changing.

There is an important distinction between summarization of outputs and summarization of networks. The use of summary networks has resulted for two reasons: first, inability to integrate networks as discussed above, and second, using summary networks to display results to management.

It appears that better methods are possible for both needs, and it is believed that the elimination of summary networks will remove a number of confusing and conflicting factors resulting from their use.

Figure 13 depicts an integrated Hughes–PERT system in operation. The levels of breakdown are corresponding closely to the organizational arrangement identifying the responsibility of a given government agency, company or a division. Each contractor analyzes and integrates his program network on his computer, obtaining activity details plus precise tasks.

In addition, a tape containing task interface summary information is prepared and transmitted to the government agency which then integrates the total system network and derives the summary reports for all levels shown. Most important is the interface feedback to each contractor, giving him the updated predictions for all incoming interfaces affecting his operation.

The benefits of Hughes–PERT increase as networks are integrated to cover the total scope of a large program. Good planning is necessary to enable integration of networks which should be accomplished automatically by the computer. One-step summarization to task interface elements appears to offer a feasible solution to the need for some reduction in the size of networks to be integrated. Results from the integrated network should be summarized for management display rather than summarizing networks.

CONCLUSION

A dynamic planning and monitoring system is vital to rapid success in achieving the desired industrial growth of emerging countries. Such a system must accommodate rapid changes and show the effects of complicated interdependencies between various types of industry. To be most useful, the system must take full advantage of data-processing machines. And, finally, a practical planning and monitoring system must utilize reliable, available information.

The system described in this paper fulfils all of these requirements. The basic framework has been proved by several years of operation in military weapon system management within the United States. The machine-prepared planning documents which are prepared for several levels of management in both tabular and graphic form, correlating time, manpower, and cost information, represent a dramatic advance in modern methods. Application of the system to industrial development programs in emerging countries will produce significant benefits in terms of maximum returns for the money invested as a result of better planning, better resource allocation, and better knowledge of the impact of current progress on the future plans.

PART TWO

RESOURCE ALLOCATION DECISIONS

6

RATIONALE FOR INVESTMENT DECISIONS IN EMERGING COUNTRIES

NORMAN N. BARISH

Professor and Chairman, Department of Industrial Engineering and Operations Research, New York University

THE rationale for investment decisions in emerging countries by entrepreneurs whose primary motivations are profit is generally comparable to those in the more technologically advanced countries. However, the values of important parameters in the decision model are quite different in the underdeveloped areas and the investment preferences are therefore markedly dissimilar.

The rationale for government investment policy is generally more complicated than for entrepreneurial investment in both the emerging and technologically advanced countries. This additional complication is emphasized in the emerging countries where the problems of promoting economic growth and of evaluating social desirability are made more difficult by various economic, cultural, and political conditions which do not generally exist in the more technologically advanced countries.

DEFINITIONS AND OBJECTIVES

Investment decisions, for the purposes of this paper, cover those decisions of entrepreneurs (individuals and companies) and governmental agencies which commit funds for non-consumption expenditures. Non-consumption expenditures are those in which the benefits are expected to accrue in future years. This definition of an investment expenditure from the planning point of view is at variance with the usual accounting or tax conventions. Expenditures for research, education, and long-term promotional activities are usually treated as expenses by accountants and tax authorities. However, from the economic planning point of view, these expenditures represent investments as important or more important to the long-range future wealth of the enterprise and the nation than investments in fixed assets.

Although the goals of entrepreneurs and governments are varied, the investment decisions of all should be guided by an attempt to be most economical in achieving these goals. The resources available for achieving goals are usually limited. Investment decisions involve an allocation of these resources. These decisions should advance the individual, company, or government progress towards these goals as rapidly as possible, whether the goals are economic, cultural, religious, social, or political.

The objectives of entrepreneurial investment in emerging countries are similar to those in more industrialized countries. By and large, enterprisers will try to make as much money as possible. Thus, business decisions will usually be made with an eye to their effects on profits: profits in the long run as well as immediate returns. This is not to deny, however, that individuals will have many other subsidiary motivations. Thus, one will find individuals who will invest in land or other assets for sentimental reasons in both the industrialized and the emerging nations.

PROSPECTIVE RATE OF RETURN CRITERION

A simple and widely used measure of the prospective profitability of an investment is the expected rate of return. Thus, other things being equal, investors will prefer to invest capital funds in countries and projects which will yield the highest expected rates of return. However, variations in the risk of the alternative investments being considered prevent practical application of this oversimplified single criterion basis for investment decision making. An investment involving very little risk and promising a 15 per cent expected return may be much more desirable than an investment promising a 20 per cent expected return, but involving large risks, if the size of the possible loss is large.

M is offered the opportunity to wager $50,000 on a throw of one true die. If the die shows two, M will receive $1,000,000. If it shows any other number, M will lose $50,000. Using expected profit as the criterion for the decision, M should accept this offer. Since the die will show two once in six throws on the average, the expected profit of the offer is one-sixth of $1,000,000 minus five-sixths of $50,000. This amounts to an expected profit of $125,000. Nevertheless, if $50,000 represents M's entire net worth, M would be loathe to take advantage of this offer despite its large expected profit. However, if the wager and the reward were both reduced to 5 per cent of their original sums, say $2500 and $50,000 respectively, M would accept the offer. The loss of $50,000 represents more than twenty times the loss of $2500 to M because $50,000 is M's entire net worth. However, to a person with a net worth of one or two million dollars, the loss of $50,000 might represent just about twenty times the loss of $2500.

This example illustrates the principle that expected or average rate of return calculations are only valid when the absolute size of the maximum loss is insignificantly small relative to the net worth of the person or business and its ability to withstand the loss without serious ill effect. As the size of the maximum possible loss becomes significant, there is a reduction in the value of the proposal to the enterprise. The magnitude of this reduction in value as the size of the possible loss increases varies with individual attitudes and the financial condition of the business as well as the magnitude of the risk.

MAIN ARGUMENT

The main argument of this paper is that:

1. The significant differences in parameter values between the emerging and the advanced countries are those which affect:

    (a)   The expected return on investments.

    (b)   The risks of investments.

2. High expected rates of return are generally available on many prospective investments in emerging countries.

3. The greater the risks involved in capital investment decisions, the higher will be the expected rate of return which a private investor will demand before making investments.

4. The values of the parameters determining the risk of investment in emerging countries are different than in the more developed countries. These parameter values cause the risks in making capital investment decisions to be greater in the newly emerging countries than in the more industrialized ones.

5. Desirable governmental action can change the values of some of these parameters to reduce the risk and thus make the expected rates of return attractive to potential investors.

6. Governmental capital investments should be concentrated in those types of projects which will result in parameter changes which will create the widest reduction in investment risks and will channel private initiative and investment into activities which will best promote the country's economic and non-economic objectives.

LARGE RISKS AND HIGH RETURNS

When the absolute size of the maximum possible loss is significant relative to the potential investor's net worth, he will generally demand a higher expected rate of return the more risky the investment. The situation in most emerging countries is that very attractive expected rates of return are available for prospective investments, but the risks are unusually high. Capital investments are usually large enough to represent a significant portion of the net worth of the individual or company making the investment. In many cases, high expected or average rates of return will therefore not provide a sufficient incentive for large-scale investment because the risks will be too great and cannot be averaged out.

I therefore propose to examine the nature of the principal factors which create these risks in emerging countries and touch upon the types of government action and investment programs which may be undertaken to reduce them. The following factors appear to be pre-eminently important in determining the magnitude of investment risks in many emerging countries:

1. Shortage of management, technical, and labor skills.
2. Difficulty in forecasting and evaluating.
3. Economies of scale and shortage of capital.
4. Current size of markets.
5. Technological balance and economic dependency.
6. Social and cultural conditions.
7. Political conditions.

SHORTAGE OF MANAGEMENT, TECHNICAL, AND LABOR SKILLS

Skilled labor of all kinds is usually in short supply in newly emerging economies. Lack of skill on the part of management and workers at all levels results in poor supervision, poor management practice, poor technical design, poor worker performance. All of these, combined with make-work tendencies of labor, keep productivity low and make cost-estimating very difficult and uncertain in emerging countries.

Investment in education is the answer to many of these labor-skill problems. Although businesses can do much, the largest share of this investment in education must be made by governmental agencies. The formal and informal educational patterns in industrialized countries are not suitable for duplication in emerging countries.

Efficient educational investment patterns will depend upon the social and political as well as the economic status of the emerging country and will change as these conditions change and the educational level is raised.

DIFFICULTY IN FORECASTING AND EVALUATING

A necessary prerequisite to a capital investment decision by government and private individuals is a forecast of revenues and other benefits and of costs and other disutilities as well as an evaluation of the risks and overall desirability of the investment.

A private investor requires estimates of expected income and expected costs to estimate expected profits. Estimates of expected income require forecasts of sales and prices which are based upon the market conditions which are expected to prevail in the future. However, statistical and other facts about markets in the emerging countries are usually very limited. Estimating future costs in these countries is also extremely difficult. The relatively limited availability of all kinds of labor, technical, and managerial skills as well as the scarcity of all kinds of equipment, spare parts, power, and transportation facilities, etc., make it very difficult to predict if or when there will be a critical cost producing shortage of any of these items. In addition, the requirements of other investment programs may cause the price of those input requirements which are available to sky-rocket.

Thus, the risks involved in investment decisions in newly emerging countries are greater than the risks in more advanced economies and it is more difficult to evaluate their magnitude. There is much more limited experience in the preparation of the analyses required for making investment decisions and, therefore, less knowledge of the pitfalls, some of which may be peculiar to the local economy. The managerial and technological talent required for successful enterprise is usually scarce and not sufficiently experienced, adding to the difficulty of forecasting future performance.

Government investment in the development of statistical data collection and reporting systems can be very helpful in meeting many of these difficulties. The system should include basic economic and technical data on a regular basis as well as co-ordinative information on the plans and programs of the private and governmental organizations which will affect the future availability of resources.

ECONOMIES OF SCALE AND SHORTAGE OF CAPITAL

Modern technology frequently requires large-scale operation if production is to be efficient. Large-scale operation requires that large amounts of capital be accumulated to build and operate these facilities. Moreover, the capital requirements for production in newly emerging countries are frequently considerably higher than for equivalent production in the more advanced economies. There are several reasons for this situation. Equipment and facilities and spare parts must be shipped from distant countries in many cases. This results in high shipping and delivery costs. Foreign technical talent must be imported when it is not available and these foreign consulting fees can be costly. When commercial transportation facilities and power are not available, they must be provided for directly by the new enterprise. Inventories of all kinds must frequently be larger than in developed economies because of the long time it takes to obtain replacements of the raw materials and components required for the production operation.

Many newly emerging countries have frequently not been too successful in channeling capital funds into productive industrial investment. Some of the reasons for this situation are the preferences of many private investors for the liquidity, flexibility, and security which items like real estate frequently provide. Another factor is the lack of development of financial institutions capable of meeting the capital needs of productive industry.

Government action and perhaps direct investment can promote the development of financial institutions with policies and resources which are adequate to meet the nation's productive industrial

I

requirements. The government can also discourage some non-productive expenditures of capital by such devices as shifting more of the tax burden to land relative to other sources and depressing consumption of luxuries by placing high import duties and restrictions on these items. (Most luxury items in newly emerging economies are imported.) In some cases, the channeling of funds into productive investment can be encouraged by income tax laws which permit rapid amortization of these investments.

It is usually economically more feasible for the newly emerging countries to rely upon the more advanced countries for most basic research. However, some government sponsorship of research into ways of adapting basic scientific findings to the peculiar resources or needs of the newly emerging country or to solve unique national problems can frequently prove very fruitful, especially in the field of natural resource development. Using research to take advantage of a country's natural resources may help overcome some of the problems when the economy of large-scale operation cannot be obtained.

CURRENT SIZE OF MARKETS

The size of the market for the production of industrial products is usually smaller in the newly emerging countries than in the more advanced economies. Not only is the number of potential consumers frequently limited in number but also their potential purchasing power is restricted by low *per capita* income and therefore low purchasing power. The effects of inflation will frequently compound this market problem.

An important way in which governments can counteract the effects of limited potential customers and purchasing power is through the establishment of regional marketing agreements encompassing a number of countries in the area. These can substantially increase the rate of industrial growth of the countries.

To counteract the effects of market size and uncertainty in a newly developing economy, some governments have in the past given special protection or guarantees to companies or individuals willing to invest in a new industry. These incentive arrangements have sometimes involved granting of exclusive monopoly privileges for varying periods of time to a company willing to make the investment.

TECHNOLOGICAL BALANCE AND ECONOMIC DEPENDENCY

The process of technological advance in the emerging countries differs considerably from what has taken place over a span of many years in the more advanced countries. In the countries of western Europe and the United States, development of new and more efficient means of producing goods and services occurred in a relatively smooth pattern in which the facilities for each successive improved stage were produced by the existing resources of human skills, capital equipment, and facilities. For the emerging countries, such a gradual process for the development of modern technology would generally be very uneconomic and be considered undesirable from other points of view. This is what makes most emerging countries so dependent upon the more advanced economies regardless of the natural resources or financial wealth of the country.

As it develops industrially and the volume of its international trade grows, the emerging country will also increase its dependency upon other nations. A major portion of the economic output of emerging economies is usually in the agricultural and extractive industries. The major portion of the products of these industries is sold to the more advanced countries for further processing and consumption. The newly emerging country thus becomes economically very dependent upon the purchases of the more advanced countries. A mild economic downturn in a more advanced country can then cause a very substantial decline in the demand for the emerging country's exports. This can result in a highly disrupting repercussion in the entire economy of the emerging country. These repercussions will have serious effects on all industry in the emerging country and therefore will represent risks and uncertainties which all investments must bear.

One of the advantages of having as balanced a development as possible in a newly emerging economy is that the complementary expansions which are developing concurrently help provide markets for each other's products and reduce the requirements of each enterprise to sell its products abroad and to purchase items abroad. With sources of supply of raw materials closer at hand and with markets for their products closer at hand, the risks and uncertainties in the business activity are reduced.

Many theories of the economic growth of countries through various stages have been forcefully expounded by economists and historians and most of them have very reasonable elements. However, the fact remains that our scientific knowledge of growth patterns is very fragmentary. We need more measurable statistical knowledge of the operational characteristics of a developing economy and better methods of analysis to evaluate alternative possibilities for influencing the direction and rate of that growth.

In any case, government policies to spur investment and growth should be based on analyses of the pertinent available economic advantages and resources rather than an attempt to follow a given theoretical pattern or a pattern that has appeared to work successfully elsewhere. Each investment project should be analyzed in terms of the economic and other factors in the country rather than evaluated by the analogy that "what has worked well in one emerging country will be good in another". Wherever possible, governments should use statistical studies to assist in forecasting the effects of alternative policies and in promoting development patterns which will be both rapid and stable. (Input–output analysis can sometimes be very helpful in this connection if it is carefully applied and its limitations are understood.) An analysis by Chenery of the patterns of industrial growth reveals some interesting relations about patterns of resource allocation.* The general conclusion of this study is that economic growth is likely to be accelerated by anticipating desirable changes in resource use and retarded by institutional arrangements

* H. B. Chenery, "Patterns of Industrial Growth", *American Economic Review*, 50, No. 4, 624–54, (September 1960).

or government policies that inhibit such changes. Some of the specific conclusions of this study are:

1. When allowance is made for variations in size of country, there is a well-defined growth pattern for individual sectors of the economy. The greatest variation in output levels is in industries producing machinery, transport equipment, and intermediate goods, where economies of scale are most important. Differences in factor endowments are reflected mainly in the variation in proportions of imports and domestic production in these sectors. Where a country deviates considerably from the normal output pattern, there is some evidence that lagging sectors of industry are likely to grow more rapidly than normal and tend to approach the normal pattern.

2. Leading sectors are likely to be industries in which import substitution becomes profitable as markets expand and capital and skills are acquired.

3. While the analysis focused on the similarities in the patterns of growth, it also revealed the need to consider the factors peculiar to each situation.

SOCIAL AND CULTURAL CONDITIONS

When an economy shifts the basis of its technology abruptly, many dislocations of social and cultural patterns occur which would not be serious problems if the changes were more gradual.

Emerging countries usually have social and cultural groups which are relatively self-sufficient compared with the highly inter-dependent structure of society in the more advanced industrial economies. (Consider the dependency of the American housewife on the appliance manufacturer, the appliance repairman, the electric power company, and the telephone company.) This change in the self-sufficiency of traditional units in the society of an emerging country creates difficulties and requires adjustments. The traditional forms of organization break down and new social, industrial, and government organization structures must be developed. The new developments, of course, may cause disturbing frictions and tensions.

Private ownership of major capital investments is complicated in many of the emerging countries by traditional reluctances to the separation of ownership and management of business enterprise. This seriously limits the possibilities for amassing the large amounts of capital necessary for much modern enterprise.

People will not invest in stock ownership in the corporation to any great extent when they are used to handling their own financial affairs personally or having them handled by only personal friends or relatives. They are also inhibited from making stock investments when they are worried about the security of investments in the country. Another inhibiting factor is sometimes provided in places in which money is not the usual medium of exchange. Also, when productive enterprise is traditionally tied in with family, village, or tribal organization, investment in the corporation organized on a broader social scale will be handicapped.

Well-designed, government-sponsored educational programs can be the answer to some of these problems. Going slow and carefully in a planned manner when critical, sensitive, cultural patterns are being changed will usually result in faster overall progress than making such changes abruptly with consequent turmoil.

POLITICAL CONDITIONS

A changeable political climate puts a premium on investments which are liquid and flexible and therefore less risky.

When inflation continues year after year those investments which provide a good hedge against inflation, such as real estate, are less risky. However, these are not the types of investment most productive of economic growth.

A stable government which has strict respect for property rights is conducive to more effective channeling of capital resources to the most productive investment possibility. When government is not stable and property rights not secure, the risks of investment in equipment, plants, and facilities are greater than the risks in the inventory investment involved in merchandising enterprise. Inventories can be hidden. They can be transported to other places.

They can be sold more readily. The normal turnover period is considerably less than the capital recovery period for investment in facilities. Inventory investment can therefore be more readily adjusted to meet changes in demand.

Security of property rights is also very important in newly emerging economies because much foreign exchange is required to purchase equipment and technical skills abroad, and the foreign exchange resources of these new economies are likely to be limited in comparison to these requirements. Thus, when property rights and local investment are not secure, the wealthy groups in these countries are more likely to spend their available funds on non-productive consumption goods. Since many of these non-productive items are purchased from abroad, this further depletes the foreign exchange available for productive investments which require purchases from the more industrialized countries.

Some newly emerging countries have government regulations to protect labor which increase the risks and uncertainties of investments by reducing the ability of the entrepreneur to adapt his operations to meet future, unforeseeable conditions. Some of these laws make it practically impossible to discharge workers, change work methods, or eliminate feather-bedding work practices. (It is true that many advanced economies operate with some of these same problems, but, in their formative growth years, these problems were generally minimal.) Legislation which will reduce some of these risks and at the same time protect the rights of the worker will promote capital investment and economic growth.

GOVERNMENT PLANNING TO PROMOTE PRIVATE INITIATIVE

Although the criteria used for government and entrepreneurial investment decisions should be different, they should both advance the economic growth of the country. Government action and investment should be designed so that rational private investment will increase and will flow into economically and socially desirable directions. Centralized government planning is necessary to accomplish this. However, centralized government operation and control of those businesses which can be developed and operated under free market initiative (regardless of who are the ultimate owners) is not conducive to most rapid, long-run economic advancement.

The persons with large personal incomes and savings in the emerging countries, which are the only domestic source of private capital for investment, are frequently more inclined to invest their money in real estate or to hoard it rather than take the risks and uncertainties of investment in enterprise. This is sometimes used as the basis for arguing that government-enforced savings and investment and public ownership are necessary to promote industrialization in these countries. Moreover, when projects are on a very large scale, private co-ordination of all the educational, social, cultural, and public health aspects which are important to the success or failure of the project becomes difficult. Without public effort on a co-ordinated basis, some aspects of these requirements may be neglected and major investments may fail to achieve their objectives. Whether public ownership is required to achieve these co-ordinations frequently depends upon the local situation.

Government action and investment should be concentrated in those fields which will channel private initiative and investment into areas which will best promote economic growth and the non-economic objectives of the individual and nation. In the course of the discussions in this paper, various proposals have been made for government action to reduce investment risks and thereby make investment opportunities attractive to private investors. Government investment resources should thus be concentrated in those areas where the results of these investments will reduce the risks associated with further productive investment by non-governmental investors. Obviously, the relative importance of the proposals mentioned in this paper will vary with the economic, political, social, and cultural situation in the emerging country. Careful, impartial evaluation is required in each case to determine the relative priority which should be assigned to each factor.

7

INDUSTRIALIZATION INCENTIVES FOR UNDERDEVELOPED COUNTRIES

JOEL DEAN

Professor of Business Economics, Graduate School of Business
Columbia University, and Joel Dean Associates

PROLOGUE

OVER the past 150 years, a body of economic theory applicable to an industrialized society has been developed. Only within the last two decades, however, has this rich body of economic science begun to have its full impact on the business community through the development of Managerial Economics. The development of these new applications of economics has been of great benefit to the business community by making available to executives the powerful tools that the economic theory and statistical science have fashioned. Economic theory itself has also benefited from enriched knowledge of the real world whose behavior theory tries to analyze, guide, and ultimately predict.

During the last two decades, much attention has been given to the problems of the underdeveloped countries. Much progress has been made in dealing with these problems. Overwhelmed, however, at times by their complexity, we have overlooked the accumulated body of theory generated in industrialized societies. We have neglected the know-how that Managerial Economics has built up during its relatively short life for adapting theory into tools that can be used to solve the problems industry faces.

Underdeveloped economies have many unique features requiring new approaches, fresh insights, and different remedies. Nevertheless, many of their economic problems are still amenable to the body of knowledge already built up in industrialized societies. Managerial Economics and management sciences can make a great contribution to the progress of these underdeveloped countries, not only by scientific analysis of the unique problems they face, but also by application of tested solutions for familiar problems. The problem is to determine to what degree our own experience is applicable, i.e. whether remedies that have worked in the industrialized countries of the Western world can, with the necessary adjustments, be transferred.

This paper examines a promising kind of industrialization incentive for an underdeveloped economy. Tax incentives to industrialize and modernize have been largely confined to industrial nations of western Europe where they have worked extremely well.

They can, I think, also be applied in some of the underdeveloped nations. The nations I am thinking of still have shockingly low real *per capita* incomes measured by either U.S. or western European standards. In these countries, however, industrialization has already begun; the governments are a more or less important channel of revenue collection and service disbursement; the prime objective is to raise income levels by triggering the industrialization process.*

I. WHAT FORM OF INCENTIVE IS PROPOSED

What is here proposed is a program of tax incentives for industrialization and equipment modernization which takes the form of a speed-up in the tax write-off of new productive equipment. In purest form the proposal is that investments in new equipment would for tax purposes be written off as fast as the firm chose—expensing them either in the year acquired or as soon thereafter as elected.

* Most of Latin America and India, for example, would fall into these categories.

This proposal would permit tax write-offs to keep ahead of the capital wastage caused by obsolescence and by inflation rather than fall seriously short as is common now.* The speed-up would produce both the incentives and the funds to replace obsolete equipment.

The powerful incentive toward industrialization and modernization that would be supplied by cash-flow tax amortization in its pure form needs to be modified and tailored to fit the development objectives, stage of economic maturity, industrial structure and tax system of the particular country. Tailoring can take the form of restrictions on the scope, the magnitude, or the timing of acceleration. As to *scope*, for example, the speed-up of tax write-offs might be restricted thus:

1. Confined to equipment (i.e. excluding buildings).
2. Confined to equipment that is new.
3. Confined to equipment installed in industrial companies (i.e. excluding regulated public utilities, petroleum, and mining companies).
4. Confined to processing and production equipment (i.e. excluding marketing and distribution).

As to *magnitude*, discretionary tax write-off might, for example, be restricted as follows:

1. Confined to an amount which bears some specified relationship to the firm's existing depreciation charges.
2. Require that any gain from sale of replaced equipment be taxed as current income (i.e. the difference between receipts and tax book value).
3. Require that whatever tax write-off the company elects shall also be the basis for reporting to stockholders.

---

* There would, of course, be great virtue in eliminating inflation in the underdeveloped as well as the developed countries. If there is to be inflation, however, the long-run interests of the countries involved make it preferable that the indirect tax of inflation does not fall on investments being relied upon to bring living standards up.

As to *timing*, the potential variations are many. A few examples are:

1. Gear the speed-up to existing estimates of depreciation life by means of double, triple, or quadruple declining-balance tax write-offs. (A politically realistic concession to accounting traditions which can attain the essential economic objectives of cash flow depreciation.)

3. Grant a substantial initial tax depreciation allowance, followed for the remaining book life by whatever tax depreciation routines are politically acceptable.

3. Turn the spigot of fast tax depreciation on or off in some systematic relationship to national budgetary deficits or levels of employment or surplus.

This principle of speeded tax write-off as a modernization incentive is capable of modifications, either at the outset or through time, to achieve the optimum balance among these objectives: (1) industrialization, (2) modernization, (3) minimization of cyclical fluctuations in business activity, (4) minimization of cost to the government through postponement of revenue, and (5) legislative and administrative convenience.

II. WHY MODERNIZATION INCENTIVES ARE PROPOSED

The typical underdeveloped country is trying to lift itself by its own boot straps. There is a determination to industrialize and to increase *per capita* incomes. This determination, while admirable, frequently leads to policy measures which are inimical to full and efficient use of an enterprise system in the country's economic development. More and more economic regimentation is therefore required. And even then the looked-for gains in industrialization and in income frequently fail to materialize.

Discriminatory Treatment

One expression of a nation's economic policy is its structure of taxation. In some underdeveloped countries the tax system discriminates against the very industries upon whose growth increased incomes depend. In part, this discrimination arises from inefficiency or corruption in the collection of taxes. Consequently, in developing the tax structure, the test of a good tax has often been whether collection is politically painless rather than whether the tax provides socially desired incentives for economic development.

To offset the resulting anti-industry tax-discrimination, governments in some underdeveloped countries have granted various kinds of individualized *ad hoc* concessions.

Some experience with corrective measures of this kind indicates that they often create further imbalances and distortions which move the country further away from the efficiency of allocation of resources and of competitive controls that are obtainable from a free market.

Superiorities of Tax Incentives to Investment

The practical attainment of the industrialization and growth aspirations of the new nations depends fundamentally upon their success in inducing capital investment and in guiding this investment into the industrial developments which are most economic at this stage of the nation's development.

One efficient and proven way to entice and to guide industrialization investment is by means of tax incentives in the form of an acceleration of depreciation for tax purposes. This solution has for several reasons particular promise for underdeveloped nations who in this era seek optimum speed of industrialization.

In contrast to the patchwork of *ad hoc* concessions which they should replace, tax incentives to investment operate impersonally, automatically, and efficiently. Equally available to all firms in any specified industry, this kind of depreciation speed-up would replace the arbitrariness and discrimination characteristic of the economic measures of many underdeveloped countries.

A second superiority of an impersonal tax incentive over the individualized and personally administered patchwork of concessions and permits is that it taps a new source of investment capital.

Investment opportunities would be made more attractive for smaller American firms who are often unable to successfully negotiate concessions. These small firms, because of greater flexibility and adaptability, are often able to better utilize the plethora of labor and the ingenuity of native partners than can larger American firms, predisposed as they are toward capital-intensive mass-production.

A third superiority of tax incentives over more personalized investment stimulation and direction is that they economize a scarce resource—native bureaucrats. Planning, stimulating, and directing the capital investment of an entire economy is an intricate job which would outstrip the massed professional competence available in a highly industrialized nation. For an underdeveloped country, despite its more primitive economy, releasing the skilled and experienced bureaucratic manpower to effectively administer the nation's investment expansion program is impossible. The economic decisions as to how much and at what places to invest for optimum industrialization are intricate. If they are wrong the cost is great, even though hidden. The consequences of incompetence is at best costly and at worst catastrophic.

In contrast, an appropriate system of fast tax write-offs can provide investment incentives at tiny administrative cost which operate automatically to produce economic choices concerning the amount and allocation of capital investment which are, on balance, correct. Firms whose products and services are most urgently needed and hence promise most rapid growth and highest rates of return will, under this plan, be stimulated to invest. Thus the pattern of investment will automatically reflect the pattern of the nation's needs in so far as these are mirrored by spending. Thus tax incentives save a particularly scarce resource in underdeveloped countries, economic administration, by providing a solution which is inexpensive compared with alternatives which have far less promise of success.

The efficacy of liberal tax depreciation in stimulating industrial development and in speeding the replacement of obsolete equipment has been demonstrated by the experience of industrialized Western economies. The transferability of this experience to the industrializable new economies requires study. And the precise ways in which investment incentives need to be tailored to the peculiar requirements of a particular nation is a problem which requires much study and is beyond the scope of this paper. Our concern here rather is to show the main thrust of the potential promise of tax incentives for solving one of the most pressing problems of this generation.

The Problem of Budget Balancing

In the initial stages of a tax incentive program, a question which is particularly crucial for an underdeveloped nation is how the government should make up for the revenues thus postponed. Clearly, the revenue is not, as is commonly claimed, lost. Instead, it is merely deferred. For the proposed tax incentive is in effect a self-liquidating, interest-free government loan. Ultimately, the resulting growth of income and widening of the tax base will more than restore the tax income thus deferred. Meantime, the temporary impact of accelerated amortization upon budget-balancing can be mitigated in various ways, three of which are important.

1. The amount of initial postponement of tax revenue could be curtailed by restricting the kinds of investments and the surrounding circumstances of eligibility, as described in more detail later.

2. A reduction in other kinds of subsidized investment incentives could substitute for the speed-up of tax depreciation. The result might be a temporary reduction of government revenue which would be small compared with the considerable improvement in the allocation of resources.

3. A temporary step-up in foreign aid. If tax incentives for investment are applied on a sufficient scale to be helpful in industrializing a new nation, it is likely that initially a greater amount of financial assistance from outside the economy may be necessary—in order to avoid inflation and to give the tax incentives an opportunity to produce their desired step-up of investment.

III. HOW FAST TAX WRITE-OFFS WOULD WORK

The economic mechanism of the stimulus to modernization investment created by speeded tax amortization is most clearly seen in its pure form—cash-flow write-off. Modifications of this most liberal form of tax depreciation work the same way. Hence, this analysis, which is focused on cash-flow write-off, applies also and only with lesser force to less liberalized tax depreciation.

Two views of its operation are summarized in this section: the mechanism and then three problems it solves.

A.   MECHANISM OF STIMULUS TO INVESTMENT

Speeded tax amortization stimulates investment and steps up equipment modernization by four reinforcing mechanisms:

1. It makes an investment more attractive by increasing its after-tax rate of return and reducing its risks.

2. It increases the supply of funds practically available for such investments.

3. It deploys investment funds into industrialization and equipment modernization and away from "non-productive" investments such as foreign securities, speculative activities or precious metals. These investments absorb much of the savings of underdeveloped countries under present tax systems.

1. Increases Attractiveness of Industrialization

Speeded tax amortization increases the incentive for industry to modernize equipment in two ways: (1) by stepping up the after-tax rate of return on the investment, and (2) by reducing the risk of any particular investment.

The main economic mechanism by which speeded tax amortization stimulates modernization is by making such investments more attractive through raising the rate of return on investments in advanced equipment which replaces obsolete equipment. The rate of return that matters is the after-tax earnings from the added efficiency of the new equipment. Speed up of tax write-off increases the after-tax rate of return, because of the time value of the money which is released and put to productive work inside the firm by postponement of income taxes. This postponement results because writing off the full amount of the new equipment investment for tax purposes in the first year reduces taxes that year. It increases them by a corresponding amount later.

Speeded tax write-off also makes modernization investments attractive by reducing their risk. The hazard that the new equipment will become obsolete long before the end of its physical life is reduced by assuring that the amortization of the capital outlay for tax purposes (and for stockholder reporting purposes) will be completed early in the life of the asset rather than continuing for years after it has become obsolete.

There are, of course, other risks than obsolescence. Some of these risks probably are a much more important deterrent to investment in underdeveloped countries than obsolescence; e.g. political instability or suppressed inflation which taxes through profit and price controls. Fast write-offs would not lessen these hazards. In most cases, however, fast write-offs would step up willingness to take such risks by permitting a more rapid recovery of investment.

2. Increases Supply of Corporations' Investible Funds

A second way in which speeded tax amortization stimulates modernization is by increasing the supply of funds which, as a practical matter, are viewed by management as available for investment.

This increase comes from three sources:

(a) more after-tax cash generation by businesses, because the cash outflow of income taxes is immediately reduced (and later augmented);

K

(b) more funds directly available for investment, because they are sheltered from divided pay-out and hence from personal tax leakage and personal consumption outlays;

(c) bigger minimum reinvestment funds, because of the tendency to make capital expenditures at least equal depreciation, which will be bigger.

The first of these sources of funds, bigger immediate *after-tax* corporate cash generation, is an obvious consequence of faster tax write-offs. In addition, speeded amortization eventually increases the *before-tax* cash generation of corporations because of cost reduction through greater efficiency.

The second source, reduced exposure to dividend dissipation, flows from accounting folkways. The "mores" make book depreciation (for stockholders) follow tax depreciation. Book depreciation ear-marks part of the firm's cash generation. Designating more of the cash flow as a provision for depreciation keeps it from being viewed as net profits, which are available for distribution. Funds distributed to stockholders are eroded by personal income taxes. What funds are left are saved only at personal discretion. In addition, because of the lack of well-developed capital markets, distributed earnings fre-quently do not, in the new nations, find their way back to industry. In contrast, if there were cash-flow write-offs, the whole amount would be automatically saved initially, inside the business firm, uneroded by taxes and available for capital formation.

This augmentation of available funds is caused by adherence to accounting conventions, legal restrictions, pay-out policy, and institutional considerations rather than actual cash availability. These considerations may change through time, and this source of additional investment funds dry up. However, an initial augmenta-tion of funds would occur at a critical period in the history of many of the underdeveloped countries.

Speeded amortization can augment funds available for moderniza-tion investments as a practical matter from a third source: by raising the corporation's reinvestible minimum. Corporate management quite generally views depreciation reserves as a minimum level of investment "to stay even". Fast write-offs raise this minimum. This third source of increase in the practical supply of corporate investment funds is also cultural in origin, but it is a deep-seated practice not likely to be quickly modified and, in fact, not yet modified even in the U.S.

If we had perfect capital markets, and no managerial inhibitions about capital sources, corporations would get from the equity and debt security markets whatever capital they could profitably invest. Under such circumstances, the effects of fast tax write-off on augmentation of internal supplies of investible funds would not matter. We do not, however, have perfect capital markets, even in the highly industrialized nations.

Capital markets in most underdeveloped nations are quite imperfect. The inability of business enterprises to obtain from the capital market the funds which would be justified by their prospective earnings slows down the growth and industrialization, at least from the private sector. Capital markets in new nations, moreover, are likely to develop too slowly to supply the equity funds needed to attain the speed of economic growth that may be politically imperative. Financing institutions that were designed to serve a pre-industrial era require basic reorientation for the new tasks of industrialization. The development of capital markets is likely to be further slowed by inflation and by political caprice. These conditions make risks greater. They also make prices higher for both equity and debt capital through existing financial institutions, which in some countries have monopoly power in the supply of funds.

While fast tax write-offs cannot solve the whole problem of the long-term capital requirements of an underdeveloped nation, they would be a major step in solution. The alternative sources of outside financing are in such nations often inadequate and expensive. Hence, the augmentation of internal funds by fast tax write-off is a matter of practical and immediate importance.

3. Deploys Funds to Equipment Modernization

We have seen, first, that in underdeveloped nations fast tax write-offs can step up industrialization by making modernization investment more compelling because of higher after-tax returns and lower risks. Second, we have seen that the *de facto* supply of investible funds to the corporation is increased in ways that are peculiarly vital for nations in early stages of industrialization.

A third way, that fast tax write-offs will step up industrialization and modernization, is by making such investments more attractive relative to presently tax-favored alternative outlays.

At present investments to expand industrial capacity and to replace obsolete equipment are in many underdeveloped countries tax-penalized, as compared with outlays on expense accounts, agriculture, or real estate. This handicap has, in some countries, come about through folk ways of tax evasion. Because industrial plants are conspicuous and have accessible accounting records, investments in productive facilities are likely to be taxed heavily *de facto* in comparison with many other forms of investment. Whether this disparate tax treatment arises from the structure of tax rates or from the convenience of tax collection, its effect is the same, namely to distort the allocation of that nation's productive resources as compared with the pattern which would produce optimum economic development.

Accelerated tax depreciation, which would put incentives for investment in industrialization and modernization on a tax parity with these less productive outlays, would step up the flow of funds to this use by diverting it from these alternative outlays. Thus it would tend to correct the mal-allocation of the resources of the underdeveloped nation which is created by tax discrimination.

B.   THREE TROUBLESOME PROBLEMS SOLVED

Cash-flow write-offs will also solve three technical problems of tax depreciation which now deter industrialization and produce inequities in some underdeveloped nations. These three problems concern price levels, economic life, and shape of value-loss.

1. Price Levels

Inflation has in many new nations made depreciation charges based on historical cost fall short of the amount needed to replace the equipment at the higher price levels. Understatement of true capital wastage causes overstatement of real taxable profits. The real rate of corporate income taxation is thus far higher than the apparent rate, and discourages industrial investment.

2. Economic Life

Accelerating technical progress in developed countries is making the economic life of production equipment in underdeveloped as well as developed countries much shorter than its potential physical life. The result is often to spread out depreciation recovery of a modernization investment over an unrealistically long economic life, and to understate capital wastage in the crucial early years. This causes an additional overstatement of taxable profit, puffs up the real corporate tax rate above the high nominal rate, and discourages industrial investments.

3. Time-shape of Value-loss

Capital wastage is not necessarily spread evenly over a machine's life. Because of obsolescence, rising repair cost and increasing un-reliability, the loss of market value is, for much equipment, greatest in early years. Yet uniform rate of decline is conventional in accounting, and in many underdeveloped countries is mandatory in tax depreciation. This disparity in the time-shape of value-loss causes distortion in profit measurement. Because of the time-value of money, it tends to puff up effective tax rates and discourage industrialization.

While each of these three problems is capable of a separate solution, the combination of these separate solutions would, in most nations, further complicate already unwieldly tax structures. Speeded tax depreciation provides a simple single solution for all three problems.

In its purest and most powerful form, namely cash-flow write-off, fast tax amortization makes all three of these technical problems academic. Price-level risk is wiped out by immediate expensing. Economic life need not be predicted at all for tax purposes, and can be projected as the taxpayer elects. The problem of the time-shape of loss in value is avoided altogether by writing off in the first year. If the taxpayer chooses longer life, he can specify time-shape on the basis of his experience.

Speeded tax depreciation can, in various modified forms, be geared to offset any predicted rate of inflation, any shortening of economic life caused by obsolescence, or any time-shape of value-loss. It can solve all three problems because the time-value of money to industry is high. Hence, postponing taxes produces benefits which can be tailored to be the economic equivalent of the injury caused by present failures of tax depreciation to solve these three problems, which now deter equipment modernization and industrial development generally in many new nations.

IV. WHAT FAST TAX WRITE-OFFS COULD ACCOMPLISH

Cash-flow tax write-offs can speed economic growth in under-developed countries in five important ways:

A. *Economic Growth.* They can provide incentives for economic growth now often lacking in the private sectors of these economies.

B. *Technical Progress.* They are needed for exploitation of the frontiers opened by advancing technology.

C. *Productivity.* They can generate the increases in productivity necessary to support higher wages.

D. *Full Employment.* They can be an important part of a program, to eliminate unemployment and underemployment, because they step up activity in industries with potentially high productivity.

E. *Competitive Position.* They can help establish the competitive position of these countries in world markets.

A. ECONOMIC GROWTH

The rate of growth in some underdeveloped economies is dominantly determined by the rate of increase in productivity. In many of the underdeveloped as well as in the developed economies, the rate of increase in the efficiency and utilization of capacity of industrial equipment is determined by profit incentives. Liberalization of tax depreciation is a powerful economic policy instrument for stepping up the incentives of a free people to achieve optimum economic growth.

B. TECHNICAL PROGRESS

Recent scientific breakthroughs presage a technological revolution in countries where national economic policies are appropriate. To convert the dazzling opportunities of the laboratory into productivity gains and economic growth requires investment incentives powerful enough to overcome the hazards of product innovation and the risks of rapid methods obsolescence. This is as true for the underdeveloped as for the industrialized economies.

The scientific basis for advanced industrial technology is accessible to the underdeveloped countries. They have not yet fully used, however, the incentives necessary for its conversion into rising productivity and economic growth. Liberalized tax depreciation can help to increase the incentives required to shoulder risks and achieve the promise of economic growth and rising productivity.

C. PRODUCTIVITY

High productivity depends on the existence of these things: technologically advanced equipment, labor skills and incentives geared to advanced equipment, managerial competence, and adequate incentives to achieve this productivity.

The scientific foundation for stepping up worker productivity through machine modernization is already at hand. The great worldwide scientific revolution will provide many additional opportunities in the coming decade.

The managerial talent for stepping up worker productivity is also at hand in developed countries. With the proper incentives, it would be exported in larger quantities, and managerial skills would grow at a more rapid rate in the underdeveloped countries.

The labor-skill necessary for productivity increases is in short supply in most underdeveloped countries. Labor's willingness to adapt to new technology, and its ambition to advance itself by mastering the skills of a new technology, could, however, be fostered by increasing incomes generated by investments that would flow from tax incentives.

In a free economy, the incentive to invest in advanced equipment which replaces obsolete production facilities can come only from an attractive after-tax rate of return on the investment. This investment incentive is presently inadequate. This is evidenced by the failure of some of these countries to narrow their productivity disadvantage. It is evidenced also by widespread unemployment or under-employment.

D.   FULL EMPLOYMENT

Attainment of full employment is a central and indispensible part of a realistic economic program for underdeveloped countries. Full employment usually requires incentives to develop industries which will raise the productivity of labor. At rising wage rates, full employment is certainly dependent upon rising productivity. Liberalized tax depreciation will provide the incentives and the funds to replace obsolescent equipment and to generate productivity increases.

E.   COMPETITIVE POSITION

The competitive position in world markets of many of these underdeveloped countries needs improving. Some have faced balance-of-payments difficulties which all too often have erupted into foreign exchange crises. Why? Because they are high-cost competitors.

Direct attack on high costs by wage and price controls is not likely in the long run to improve the competitive position of these nations. The U.S. experience with controls indicates that wages are harder to keep down than prices. Direct attack by raising tariffs, paying export subsidies, or by exchange control is an economic policy inimical to free economic development.

A practical aid in the long-term correction of the comparative cost disadvantage of an under-industrialized nation is to supply powerful inducements for equipment modernization. Some of the alternative and apparently more direct solutions will boomerang in the long run.

8

EDUCATIONAL POLICY FOR ECONOMIC GROWTH

WILLIAM J. PLATT

Director, Management Science Division, Stanford Reseach Institute,
Menlo Park, California

ECONOMISTS and other social scientists* interested in development are devoting increased attention to human capital. In part they do so because they find that investments in human capital—in the form of education—play a hitherto underrated role in the process of economic and social growth. And growth, I need not remind you, is a stylish topic, east and west, north and south

My purpose today is to urge management scientists and systems analysts to join this inquiry. Education as a topic deserves a place in the agenda of management scientists, for many of the same reasons it is found with increasing frequency in journals of economics. Here are some reasons.

WHY EDUCATION QUALIFIES FOR OUR AGENDA

1. Education is an engine of development, playing the role of liberating talent. This property can trigger the multiplier effect

---

* A few of the social scientists active in this inquiry include Schultz, Bowman, Anderson, Houthakker, Becker, and Coombs in the United States; Edding and Albers in Germany; Martinoli in Italy; Debeauvais in France; Schmidt in Denmark; and Vaizey in the United Kingdom. See References 1 through 12 at the end of this paper.

leading to higher economic and social achievement of individuals and of societies.

2. Education is expensive, accounting for from 2 to 8 per cent of gross national products. Those of us practising the science of decision devote efforts to phenomena of much less consequence in the economic stream of things. Changes in the effectiveness or cost of education have major leverage for benefiting society.

3. International transactions in education promote understanding and help development. Education assistance from developed to lesser developed countries is an attractive form of international co-operation. Education aid is not impersonal—as assistance received in the form of productive facilities or commodities can be. It tends to build continuing international ties; to the extent that it "takes" (and it certainly modifies recipient attitudes in some way), it tends to encourage new transfusions. Since there is no commodity flowing, there are no direct strains on the economic relations among nations. Combine these attractions with its multiplier effect and with rising expectations in nascent societies, and one sees the need for more massive bilateral and multilateral programs of educational assistance and exchange.

4. Allocations of funds and other resources to education compete with and complement other investment allocations in ways that deserve research to find decision guides. There is a strong presumption of structural under-investment in education.

5. Education is a system and a set of sub-systems potentially susceptible of analysis, design, and perhaps eventually some optimization. As such, there should be more systematic ways of determining the size and mix of educational effort. Perhaps the experience of management scientists in programming problems, in leadtime studies, and in the technique of relating an output to an input can be of help in improving education effectiveness.

In this paper I will not solve education problems. I only hope to buttress some of the foregoing assertions on education's relevance to our profession's agenda. This I plan to do by reminding us where education fits in a development framework. Then we can identify major degrees of freedom in decision-making in education. Along the way I would like to offer a few approaches that may help illuminate the decision options, and, finally, to pose some of the unfinished business in education as questions that may offer fruitful challenge to management scientists.

In suggesting education as an agenda item it is important to sound for you the same warning one detects in economists' writings. All the ordinary hazards of professional inquiry are, of course, present: inadequate and often non-comparable data, extremely complex relationships between education and development, absence of social science theory related to education, and others. Further, the inquirer into education decision-making runs the added risk of questioning a relatively inviolate institution. Because this institution reproduces the culture, it may be viewed as too intimate a subject to measure and manipulate for optimization purposes. This key role of education is undeniable; it certainly does dictate caution in our prescriptions. It should not, however, proscribe sympathetic curiosity on the part of us, the unanointed.

TWO DISTINCTIONS

It is possible, conceptually at least, to distinguish between consumption and investment aspects of education. Cultivating an appreciation of the fine arts might be included under consumption, while professional or vocational education might be investment. Without signifying any lesser importance to education for consumption, we shall be dealing mainly with education for investment. The line in any case is hard to draw. To the degree consumption education liberates talent and intellect, it has the equivalent effect of an investment.

It is possible also to distinguish between maintenance and development functions of education. Maintenance functions would be those of simply regenerating the existing level and stock of human capital and culture. Since development and growth are generally accepted as desirable and necessary, there is little reason to spend time on maintenance alone. It is of interest only to the arch-conservative. Our emphasis will be upon development.

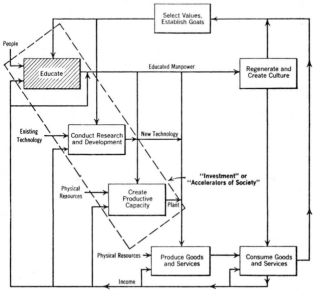

FIG. 1. *Education as a contributor to development.*

This diagram shows how education and other forms of investment contribute to development. The object of the system is "the good life", made up of cultural and economic attainment. The inputs to "educate" are people and education budgets. Controls on "educate" are values and goals of the society. Output from "educate" is educated people who perform the productive operations of the economic system, consume its goods and services, and create and regenerate its culture.

EDUCATION IN A DEVELOPMENT MODEL

The role of education in development may be visualized in Fig. 1. Education, research and development, and physical capital are the three modes of investment; investment in turn is the means by which a society regenerates itself at new levels of achievement by setting the multiplier effect into operation. As shown at the right, education for the good life, or cultural enhancement, may be distinguished from education for the economic process. The interactions between the two goals are many.

"The good life" objectives of education embrace such goals as "to develop character and taste", "to release the inner man", "to create citizens of a democracy", or "to realize fully the individual's potentialities, with civic responsibility". If an education strategist attempts to help make better decisions on the amount and content of education for these cultural objectives, he finds a qualitative playing field not easily suited to analysis. Yet even here, with the exercise of imagination he can find certain policy options that are consistent with the particular articulation of "the good life", and others that are not.

In the remainder of this paper I propose to concentrate on the role that education plays in economic development. I do this not because economic improvement is the most important aim of education. Instead the emphasis comes from a belief that there is insight to be gained by examining the linkage between education and economic development. At the same time, conclusions reached on this relationship need to be tested for compatability with the culture enhancement goals of education.

The model is a feedback system in that the levels of culture and consumption attained at any time have the effect of modifying individual and group values, and hence goals for the next round. Similarly, income from the economy flows back to all parts of the system.

Of particular interest here is the allocation of income among the three modes of investment. The decisions, implicit or explicit, that are made as to the size of these investments are critical. Clearly there also needs to be some balance among the alternative forms of investment; lest productive capacity, for example, outrun appropriately skilled manpower, or vice versa. The system can become unbalanced in culture creation, too; education may create expectations that cannot be realized in the existing cultural-political-economic environment. If means for adapting to expectations are not present, i.e. if the society or form of organization is not a self-adapting one, strife and breakdown may result.

This is not to argue solely for blandness in the balance, however. Economists are increasingly interested in conscious imbalance of a nature that may put the multiplier effect into operation more effectively than would a uniformly diluted effort that never reaches the threshold necessary for perturbing a stagnant system.

The current allocation of investment implicit in United States behavior is about $22 billion to education (more if foregone earnings of students are included), $12 billion to research and development, and $40–50 billion to plant and equipment. In the United States system hundreds of thousands of entrepreneurs remain ever alert to opportunities for profit from additional investments in plant and equipment, and to a somewhat lesser degree they also look for profitable investments in research and development. But it is not at all clear that there is an equally alert decision apparatus for determining when payoffs can come from investing additional funds in education. It seems reasonable to presume, therefore, that the marginal return to be expected from more education is higher than from either of the other two modes of investment.

How do we know education pays off? Despite a good deal of study, the satisfactory measurement of this will probably continue to occupy economists. Short leadtime demonstrations can occasionally be found.

A dramatic illustration of the profitability (both to society and to the individual) of retraining education occurs in the vocational rehabilitation program of the United States Department of Health, Education, and Welfare. Before rehabilitation training, 56,000 handicapped persons earned $15 million per year; after rehabilitation they earned $102 million per year. The additional federal income taxes paid by the group in 1 year were alone more than the $8 million cost of the training program.(13)

Findings of a more macro nature are presented by Schultz, as shown in Table 1. Note that benefits are more than ten times costs even when the latter include earnings foregone by students of employable age. The benefit to cost ratios for economies at other stages of development may well vary substantially from the United States figures. Relative scarcities of skills would differ, with corresponding variation in the ratios.

TABLE 1. *Benefits and Costs of Education in the United States, 1956*

	Male graduate of		
	Elementary	High school	College
Added lifetime income	$43,000	$64,000	$120,000
Added cost of Education (including earnings foregone)	1120	5680	13,200
Ratio: benefit to cost	38·4	11·3	9·8

Source: Theodore W. Schultz, "Education and Economic Growth", *Social Forces Influencing American Education* (National Society for the Study of Education Yearbook, 1961), p. 79.

STRATEGIES OF EDUCATION

We turn now to options facing decision-makers concerned with education's role in economic development. Scarce funds must be employed in a way compatible with the development objectives of the country. If there is not a good linkage between the education program and the development program, severe shortages or surpluses of appropriate skills are bound to occur. There can even be concomitantly under-investment in education along with waste in what is invested.

Here the decision options will be phrased from the standpoint of a local or national ministry of education interested in supporting a program of country development.

In developing education strategies it is necessary to identify the "decision variables". They fall into three groups:

A. To whom and to how many shall education be offered; through what levels?

B. What curricula, in what proportion, and under what schedule are what graduates needed? This may be termed the programming problem.

C. What educational technology and organization shall be used?

A. *To whom and to how many shall education be offered; through what levels?* Decision-makers must examine policy on universality of education. How much capacity can be provided in each level of education, taking account of the availability of qualified entrants for each, as a function of time? While nearly all countries aspire to universal education at least through primary, only those countries reasonably well up the scale of economic development can yet afford even this minimal program. Only western European countries, the Soviet Union, Israel, Japan, the United States, Canada, Australia, and New Zealand have more than two-thirds of the primary and secondary education age groups enrolled in school. In Mexico and Turkey, for example, only about 40 per cent of the males attend primary and secondary, and only 30 per cent of females.

For the purpose of studying policy toward the universality of education, a useful simplification may be that of using the economist's concept of "present value". This is the discounted net value of lifetime earnings less education costs. Discounting is a means of attaching more significance to current costs and benefits than to prospective costs and benefits in future years. In the single factor of discount rate we can reflect not only the marginal rate that capital could earn in other investments (the going interest rate), but also the risk we may wish to attach to the returns expected from education. Both interest rate and expected returns may vary with time and with the stage of economic growth reached. It is probably not necessary to establish the exact discount rate that should apply, although its amount should probably be low since risks are low. The principal use of this approach is in selecting among alternative policies for *terminal levels* of education.

An advantage in using "present value" is the ability to compress benefits and costs into a one-dimensional measure. For a com-

L

parison of the discounted values of various terminal educations in the United States, average income by amount of schooling completed has been used. If the value of an advanced degree is taken as 100, the value of other terminal education levels may be estimated as follows:

Terminal level	Present value* (discount rate 3%)
Advanced degree	100
College	85
Vocational and secondary	58
Primary	42
None	21

* Calculated from U.S. Dept. of Commerce, Bureau of the Census, *Income of Families and Persons in the United States: 1958*; (14) and Hout-hakker, "Education and Income".(4)

The present value concept may help in comparing policies of the universality of education by the method of Fig. 2. The curve at the right, "intellectual capacity", is a hypothetical expression of the maximum fraction of population equipped with sufficient inherent intelligence to absorb education of the levels shown. In a newly developing country there is such a shortage of teachers, funds, and facilities that the intellectual capacity curve will not be limiting. Instead, the limitations will appear in shortages of graduates of one level who have the prerequisites for the next level.

For a certain education budget there are various program or strategy options; for example, lines A and B in Fig. 2. The steeper curve A devotes more of available funds to intensive training of an *élite*. This is the European continental strategy of selectivity in education. The flatter curve B uses the same budget for more nearly universal training at lower levels, sacrificing to some extent the number of highly trained. This curve is the more egalitarian approach. The British colonial encouragement of education in India and West Africa appears to have observed more nearly the A-type of strategy— that of training a reasonably select pyramid capable of taking over top-level posts supported by a nucleus of middle-level personnel. When the society is in the take-off stage, a policy of moving to strategy B might be adopted to widen the educated base of the society. An example of an extremely flat curve was the pattern established in the Congo where early independence caught that society with a relatively large fraction having attended elementary school, but almost no highly trained people.

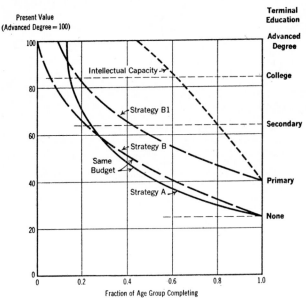

Fig. 2.   *Strategies for terminal level of education.*

A larger education budget would permit moving the whole curve to the right, as shown by line B1, thus allowing a somewhat wider latitude for strategy with respect to selectivity versus universality.

Suppose the vertical scale is recalibrated to reflect the absolute present value of the terminal level shown. We can find the value of the stock of human capital ("benefit") associated with a given strategy by taking the area under a curve. Suppose also we could measure the average *cost* of alternative terminal levels. We could again recalibrate the vertical scale and obtain, by integration, the total cost of that strategy. Repeating this, we could compare benefit/cost relationships for several alternative strategies and assuming several feasible shares of GNP or regional effort. The measurement of present value, as it may be affected by stage of development, discounting, etc., is probably so uncertain that this exercise is justified only as a means of conceptualizing the alternatives.

For educational levels above compulsory or universal attendance, a strategy must be adopted on standards for admitting and continuing students. Should social or economic status of the students' parents be important factors in admission? More objective qualifying measures are appropriate. At any rate, no progress-bent society can afford to let its most talented youth miss higher education opportunities because of economic or social or political bars. And for the same reason a society should constantly examine its own implicit prestige and value standards to see whether the most talented are naturally motivated to realize their full potentials in education.

Another strategy of education should treat what age groups should have what educational opportunities. Many are questioning an education convention of long standing: that only youth shall receive formal education. Surely the educable are not confined to the age group 6–16 or 6–21! Psychologists recognize varying rates of learning as a function of age but no absence of learning ability after age 21. The need for lifetime education is well stated by Coombs: "The frontiers of knowledge and technology will move so rapidly that much of an individual's formal training as a youth will soon become obsolete or inadequate. There must therefore be greatly enlarged arrangements and opportunities for individuals to continue learning after the termination of their formal schooling."(6)

B. *What curricula, in what proportions, with what schedule?* The curriculum and its scheduling might be designated the educational programming problem. Clearly, these must be solved in interaction with the preceding question of whom and what terminal levels. Part of the latitude in programming is fixed by the cultural and educational traditions of the country. Except in the newest of developing societies, there exists a basic curriculum in language, literature, history, and institutions of the country. It is through these that the culture is perpetuated. Mathematics and science also have taken their places as part of the curriculum everywhere. In addition to these basic subjects, the educational programmer can select the foreign language or languages to be taught. Since this selection inevitably implies some degree of orientation of students to the culture behind the language selected, the choice has at least a modicum of foreign relations significance.

In the remainder of the curriculum, the educational programmer must face the most vexing decisions of all—the amount, content, and quality of the course of study, including the humanities, public and business administration, pedagogy, fine arts, law, social sciences, natural sciences, engineering, medicine, agriculture, and vocational skills.

The systematic, thorough way of educational programming for economic development objectives is not difficult to describe. Nonetheless, it is a formidable task because of the many planning uncertainties and the detail to which it must be carried to be effective. In mature economies these programming steps may not be as necessary as in developing economies, because in the former, equilibrium conditions somewhat automatically adjust educational output to needs. However, for a mature economy to accelerate its growth greatly, it too will have to go through some of the same steps. The programming steps are as follows:

1. Outline, at least roughly, general economic development needs for future periods, preferably two or more decades ahead.*

2. Project manpower requirements associated with the economic

* The approaches in carrying out this step might use mathematical programming methods such as those described by Hollis Chenery in "Patterns of Industrial Growth".(15) These approaches make use of marginal return concepts in allocating scarce development effort in such a way that marginal expenditures in each activity contribute equally to development goals, all within constraints of resource limits.

development needs. These requirements would include the numbers of employees, professional people, and skilled self-employed needed by major skill, and the dates they are required to carry out the program of economic development. Particular attention must be devoted to determining needs for high-talent manpower.

3. Translate the manpower schedules into the types and quantities of graduates needed from all levels of education. Certain principles may assist the selection of educational tracks to accomplish the desired training. One such principle is to encourage a high degree of educational mobility and flexibility, thus leading to greater future career versatility. Applying this principle recognizes the dynamic nature of the development process and the importance of having citizens who are readily retrainable.

The informed judgment of educators must be applied to such questions as the length of education and type of facilities required to reach a given level of skills, or to train an effective teacher for a particular type or level of curriculum. Input data obtained from the educator are analogous to the technical judgments of an engineer in determining input–output coefficients. In the education case, however, objective measurement is peculiarly elusive. Perhaps a contribution of the systems analyst would be to express explicit "trial" coefficients that would lend concrete content to the arguments of educators and judgments of political leaders on these issues.

The three-step programming process will have generated some rough approximation of the *requirements* for graduates of the several terminal levels of education. The requirements curve can be plotted against the project supply (for example, on Fig. 2) to get further insight into policies and expenditures necessary to achieve the development program.

The mix of specialties (managerial, technical, commercial, agricultural, etc.) required within each terminal level of education will have been outlined by the foregoing three steps. In a centrally controlled system, fairly direct measures can be taken for guiding students of appropriate abilities into the required lines. In a system of freer educational choice, however, indirect methods must be used: incentives, subsidies, scholarships, vocational guidance by professionals and parents.

Throughout the foregoing process there must be an explicit treatment of the time dimension in creating available trained manpower. For those skills requiring several levels of education, leadtimes tend to be long, reaching as high as two decades for professions like medicine and scientific research.

For high-level talent, the effective constraint is likely to be in terms of leadtime and men rather than financial resources. Pressures become heavy for overcoming these constraints by quick training programs. The danger is that establishment of institutions for cash training programs may perpetuate low standards which produce only superficially educated personnel. A critical point is the training of teachers, and here considerable pressure is exerted. Sound decisions are probably dependent on the fibre and imaginative leadership of the educators, professional men, and politicians concerned.

Once a realistic standard is adopted for the quality of high-level personnel required in, say, year 10, this standard establishes a derived quality requirement for one strand of the preparatory college, secondary, and elementary courses. This will raise critical issues of examination policy, entrance requirements, and relationship between terminal and non-terminal courses. Much of the educational innovation required in developing countries centers on the introduction of advanced and job-preparatory terminal courses: for potential foremen, overseers, skilled workers, agricultural technicians, or farmers. Their articulation with college preparatory courses presents novel problems in terms of student motivations and the traditional biases of the country's educators.

In almost any rapidly developing country, application of the foregoing process will identify many occupational shortages for which there is insufficient educational leadtime to permit local correction. Some relief may come from recycling the whole effort, i.e. working out the calculation so that the supply of skills can more nearly meet projected demand. Even so, shortages may remain. This is where tactical adjustments such as the following must be extemporized:

1. Seek technical personnel assistance from economically more advanced countries to fill the critical gaps.

2. Offer retraining to those possessing related skills. The retraining itself may require importation of teachers who can provide required expertise. Some obvious candidates for retraining will be those with skills which are in surplus.

3. Seek opportunities to train students abroad in critical skills where local teaching facilities are inadequate. Unless multilateral or bilateral aid can be obtained, this solution could be a severe drain upon the foreign exchange position of the developing country.

In addition to helping long-range social and economic development, educational strategy can play a role in correcting short-run dislocations. In some of the newer nations of Africa and Asia there are pockets of educated and semi-educated unemployed at a time when other skills are badly needed for economic development. The educated unemployed are usually graduates of an education system whose curricula and values have been borrowed without adequate adaptation to local development needs. In these cases the educational investments that will yield earliest returns may be vocational training of the educated unemployed to provide them with some of the skills in greatest demand for economic development. Teachers, agricultural technicians, public health workers, and transportation workers are frequently those most needed. The educational leadtime of this retraining is generally short. The program, if properly communicated and related to the people's expectations, can serve to modify value symbols that had been allowed to misdevelop under the transplanted and anachronistic education system. The program can also transform frustration and unrest of the unemployed into constructive energy.

C. *What educational technology and organization?* Education is an under-researched activity. Whereas progressive industries and our defense establishment spend between 4 per cent and 10 per cent of total expenditures on research and development, the corresponding figure for education in the United States is about one-tenth of 1 per cent.(16) Fortunately, the relatively small amount of educational research is generating improvements and flexibility in the methods of pedagogy, such as educational television, radio, programmed instruction, and redeployment of faculty in team teaching and other organizational modes.

Education need no longer be confined to oral instruction by word of mouth as in class lectures or to reading textbooks. Radio may be one of the easiest ways of multiplying the reach of education in underdeveloped countries. Educational television may have interesting and effective use in education in underdeveloped countries. Where it has been used in the United States it has generally not been a substitute for the classroom teacher but rather a means of greatly increasing his effectiveness. It also permits multiplying manyfold the reach of the master teacher who is uniquely skilled at communicating a subject. In underdeveloped countries it could be a great help in offsetting teacher shortages. Under a $500,000 grant from the Ford Foundation, educational television was introduced in India in 265 secondary schools in 1961.

Self-instructional or programmed learning devices ("teaching machines") promise to raise productivity in education. Their effectiveness has been demonstrated in routine instruction in schools and industry. They free the human teacher for the more creative aspects of education. They present a program of information and questions in a planned sequence, require a response from the student, and provide an immediate check to the student on the accuracy of the response. Physically, these devices may be as simple as a set of 3×5 cards with a question on one side and an answer on the other, or as complex as a digital computer with multiple stations (displays, response mechanisms, branching programs, etc.) to accommodate many students at once. Some possible applications in economic development might include: training, standardized ability testing, and mass technical training.

Both faculty organization and administrative organization can bring higher productivity in education. In the first case new ways of deploying faculty within a school are proving to offer higher effectiveness and lower cost than traditional means. In team-teaching several instructors combine their talents to specialize in the aspects of teaching each performs best, i.e. one lectures to a large group of several classrooms together while the other instructors prepare material for small group discussions and tutoring or for programmed instruction.

The administration of schools and the provision of specialized inter-school services is another area in which organizational improvements can add to productivity by eliminating duplication and by pooling needs sufficiently to enrich the educational offerings and equipment.

Another organizational decision is that of the location policy. If rapid growth is needed, it may well be that a policy of concentrating resources and efforts for upper levels of education at a few centers will yield greater returns than a strictly equalitarian policy would. This is because only through such concentration can the threshold be reached for education to "go critical" in the sense of starting its chain, or multiplier, reaction.

These developments already allow the educational system designer to construct new configurations that will permit students to master given content at lower cost and in less elapsed time than by traditional means. In short, the coefficients that relate a needed educational output to its inputs are changing favorably. It is particularly here that the systems analyst can help the decision-maker to compare alternative policies.

SYSTEMATIC EDUCATIONAL PLANNING

Now that we have illuminated major decision areas in education we can briefly outline steps in a unifying approach to systematic planning. Excellent plans have been published for Nigeria, Pakistan, Italy, and Germany. No doubt there are others. But neither the resources nor requisite basic techniques existed to permit these studies to arrive at systematic efficient answers to the questions posed here. A more complete approach may be that described below. It is based on three related assumptions: (1) that human resources are critical determiners of economic growth, (2) that a "best assortment" of human resources can be specified for particular economic growth objectives, and (3) that educational programs and patterns of educational investment can be specified as most likely to lead to the desired human capital. While these assumptions are probably valid in a general sense, the problems of specifying an ideal mixture of manpower resources and an optimum educational program for producing this mixture are formidable indeed.

The initial effort would consist of an examination in detail of present and planned education efforts in the light of such groups of factors as (1) national goals, planned economic growth, known and projected manpower requirements, and available resources in men and money; (2) existing educational facilities, teachers, student body, etc.; and (3) curricula, job availabilities, status considerations, motivational factors, etc. These studies would seek to demonstrate, through systems analysis techniques, the character of the implicit education strategy of the country and its implications in terms of current and future budget costs and in terms of its effectiveness in meeting the country's socio-economic needs. These studies would, within the limits of available data, establish the extent to which the existing education system is providing the kinds and numbers of qualified personnel required. Examination would be made of any retraining, short course, or accelerated training schemes from the same standpoint.

Alternative strategies of education would be prepared. These would be developed in the light of the most concise statement of national socio-economic goals that can be secured and the best estimates which can be made of skilled manpower requirements over a 10-year period. The technologies and organization appropriate to the conditions of development and available resources would be selected. The analysis of the employment of manpower at various terminal levels of education may indicate apparent inadequacies of the present education program in furnishing the types of skills required and may also lead to suggestions concerning investment in retraining programs as a part of the planned strategy. Alternative strategies would be drawn up in the light both of the net requirements for skilled personnel at all levels and the potential availability of financial and human resources for educational purposes over the 10-year period under consideration.

UNFINISHED BUSINESS

The foregoing approach should reveal appropriate paths for educational investment. As the exercise is carried out, the planner will discover great uncertainties that stem from inadequate theory and data. We can already forecast some of these obstacles. They offer fruitful ground for attention of management scientists, systems analysts, and economists. Here are some of those questions:

1. What is the nature of the connections among education investments and investments in (1) science and technology, and (2) physical capital?

2. What is an efficient and a stable allocation of educational effort in the pyramid of literacy training, elementary, secondary, and higher education? As a function of stage of country development?

3. What geographic allocation of education is most effective bearing in mind (a) the need to reach the threshold of multiplier effect, and (b) urban and rural development plans?

4. How do mass communication and education complement each other in the development process and which of the two should handle what task in human resource development?

5. What are efficient trade-offs between manpower specialization versus mobility-versatility in the light of technological, social, and economic change?

6. How can education's input–output coefficients (production functions) be systematized? How are they affected by new pedagogical technology? Under what combinations of teacher-to-pupil ratio and teacher-to-facilities ratio are these coefficients maximized?

7. What basic relationships apply in international transactions in education (student and teacher exchange, educational assistance)?

8. What motivation and training are appropriate for teachers in newly developing countries in view of predictable shortages of funds and talent?

9. In curriculum design, how can preparation for advanced education be reconciled with need for useful vocational training at lower terminal levels? For example, does the design of secondary curriculum for academic preparation stultify terminal secondary education? Will the trade-off selected generate attitudes toward prestige that are not self-defeating?

10. What is an efficient trade-off in allocation of effort between adult and youth education?

From the richness of this list of unfinished business it is clear we are a long way from having a grand optimization scheme for educational investment. But the ill-structured, data-poor problem has not deterred our profession in the past. It is my hope you will join the inquiry.

REFERENCES

1. SCHULTZ, THEODORE W. "Education and Economic Growth", *Social Forces Influencing American Education* (National Society for the Study of Education Yearbook), Part II, 1961, p. 46.

2. BOWMAN, MARY JEAN and ANDERSON, C. ARNOLD. *Concerning the Role of Education in Economic Development*, a staff paper, Comparative Education Center, University of Chicago, Chicago, Ill.

3. ANDERSON, C. ARNOLD. "The Impact of the Educational System on Technological Change and Modernization", North American Conference on the Social Implications of Industrialization and Technological Change, sponsored by UNESCO, at Comparative Education Center, University of Chicago, 15–22 September 1960.

4. HOUTHAKKER, H. S. "Education and Income", *Review of Economics and Statistics*, **41**, No. 1, 24 (February 1959).

5. BECKER, GARY S. "Underinvestment in College Education." *American Economic Review*, **50** (2), 346 (May 1960).

6. COOMBS, PHILIP H. "Educational Planning in the Light of Economic Requirements", *Forecasting Manpower Needs for the Age of Science*,

(Office for Scientific and Technical Personnel, Organization for European Economic Co-operation, September 1960), pp. 25 and 31.

7. EDDING, FRIEDRICH. *Analysis of Educational Needs and Priorities for Specialized Manpower in Relation to Economic Development*, Mediterranean Regional Project No. STP-22 (Office for Scientific and Technical Personnel, Organization for European Economic Co-operation, Paris, 14 November 1960).

8. ALBERS, WILLI and EDDING, FRIEDRICH. "Financing General and Vocational Schools in the Federal Republic of Germany, 1960 to 1970" (Arbeitsgemeinschaft Deutscher Lehrerverbände, Frankfurt/Main, 1960).

9. MARTINOLI, GINO. *Trained Manpower Requirements in the Next Fifteen Years: The Role of Education in the Italian Economic Development* (SVIMEZ, Rome, 1960).

10. DEBEAUVAIS, MICHAEL and VAIZEY, JOHN. *Some Economic Aspects of Educational Development in Europe* (International Universities Bureau, Paris, 1961).

11. SCHMIDT, M. ERIK IB. "Economic Growth and the Manpower Factor", *Forecasting Manpower Needs for the Age of Science* (Office for Scientific and Technical Personnel, Organization for European Economic Co-operation, September 1960), p. 9.

12. VAIZEY, JOHN. *The Economics of Education* (Faber & Faber, London, 1961).

13. OFFICE OF VOCATIONAL REHABILITATION, DEPARTMENT OF HEALTH, EDUCATION, AND WELFARE. "The Disabled: The Rate of Vocational Rehabilitation in Improving the Economic Condition of Low-income Families", 86th Congress, 1st Session, *Characteristics of the Low Income Population and Related Federal Programs* (Washington, D.C., Government Printing Office, 1955), pp. 84–94.

14. U.S. DEPT. OF COMMERCE, BUREAU OF THE CENSUS. *Income of Families and Persons in the United States: 1958*, Current Population Reports, Series P-60, No. 33 (Washington, D.C., 15 January 1960), Table 26, p. 38.

15. CHENERY, HOLLIS. "Patterns of Industrial Growth", *The American Economic Review*, vol. **50**, No. 4 (September 1960).

16. COOMBS, PHILIP H. *Technical Frontiers of Education*, the Twenty-Seventh Annual Sir John Adams Lecture at the University of California, Los Angeles, delivered 15 March 1960.

9

ALLOCATION OF MEDICAL AND ASSOCIATED RESOURCES TO THE CONTROL OF LEPROSY

MICHEL F. LECHAT, M.D.

Leonard Wood Memorial Leprosy Research Laboratory
School of Hygiene and Public Health
The Johns Hopkins University

AND

CHARLES D. FLAGLE, Dr.Eng.

Director of Operations Research
The Johns Hopkins Hospital

INTRODUCTION

OUR purpose is to introduce to each other two groups of people, those who strive, through human organization, to control disease, and those who strive to understand human organization. We assume this introduction is in order—the authors of this paper were unknown to each other until some months ago.

We may ask in the case of leprosy what brings on this rapport of management scientist and the healer of an ancient but still wide-spread illness. The answer to this is an exciting one. Medical science has scored significant advances; effective drugs are available, but therapy must be administered to a patient over a period of several

159

years. While much remains to be learned, particularly about transmission, the problem of control of leprosy has passed from one primarily medical to an enormous one of human organization. The search for and diagnosis of patients, the administration of therapy, procuring co-operation of patients in regular clinic attendance over a period of years; these are among the principal problems to be solved.

It is our plan here to describe some of the component problems and to relate them to analogous problems which have been approached in other areas of human endeavor with some success through the management sciences.

WORLD PROBLEM OF LEPROSY

A valid estimate of the number of leprosy patients in the world is difficult to establish. Prevalence figures recently collected from all countries except China, the Soviet Union, and eastern Europe indicate a total number of about 2,000,000 registered cases.(13) During recent years, however, pilot-studies undertaken in small areas or mass surveys conducted on a national scale have usually revealed figures much higher than suspected.(1) (4) (7) (27) With the introduction of the sulfone treatment some 10 years ago, the estimated number of cases in the Congo increased from 90,000 to 210,000 between 1949 and 1953.(30) The number of patients under treatment in 1960 was 286,000.(24) In the former French Equatorial Africa the number of cases registered increased from 40,000 to 145,000 between 1953 and 1958.(26) In the small area of Polambakkam, in the south of India, 176 leprosy cases were known among the inhabitants when the Leprosy Center was established in 1955; by 1958, in the same area and among the same population, 16,000 cases had been diagnosed.(16) Since such surveys are still limited to some countries and pilot areas covering only a portion of the total population of the earth, we can assume that the number of leprosy patients in the world is much higher than indicated by the present official data. A number in the neighborhood of ten millions is a consensus generally accepted among leprologists.

Leprosy is not restricted to tropical countries or hot climates. The disease is present everywhere, with exception of some countries such as continental Chile, Ireland, Luxemburg, Kuwait, and a few others where it has not been reported. The prevalence is very irregular. In some countries of Europe, only imported cases have been observed. Leprosy is not very frequent in western Europe, the United States, Central America, North Africa, and in the Near East. In other areas, the total number of leprosy patients is high—from 10,000 to more than 100,000—and it represents up to 1 per cent of the total population of the various countries. South America, the Carribean area, and the Philippines (13) are examples of such endemicity. Moreover, in South-East Asia and Central Africa, the millions of leprosy patients may represent as much as 1 to 3 per cent of the whole population of some of the countries, 5 per cent of that of some important towns, and perhaps 10 to 15 per cent in some villages.(13) (16) (30)

TRANSMISSION

Leprosy is caused by a micro-organism, *Mycobacterium leprae*, which develops in the skin and in the peripheral nerves of humans. Very little is known about the transmission of the disease. Although the causative agent of leprosy was the first bacillus to be discovered in humans (in 1874 by Hansen in Norway), it has not been possible, unlike most of the other agents causative of disease, to cultivate it under laboratory conditions, or to inoculate it in animals or in human volunteers. These facts make laboratory research particularly difficult.

The risk of leprosy has been much exaggerated through the ages. It is now widely accepted that, in many instances, leprosy is often difficult to contract. Moreover, only the patients affected with one particular type, the so-called lepromatous leprosy, transmit the disease. It is important to point out that recent data collected by the World Health Organization indicates that in Africa only 7 per cent of the patients are affected with this type of leprosy.(12) The

M

93 per cent remaining can be considered as of little importance in the transmission of the disease, and thus are treatable as out-patients.

PROGNOSIS AND TREATMENT

It is difficult to ascertain whether the life expectancy of leprosy patients is significantly different from the whole population, at least in the areas of primitive living conditions where leprosy is prevalent. However, the most serious characteristic of leprosy is that approximately 20 to 25 per cent of patients ultimately develop deformities such as dropping of fingers, claw-hands, loss of the foot, often becoming complete invalids.(19)

Treatment is possible and effective, even in the most advanced cases. The sulfones, synthetic compounds first tried in human leprosy in the United States in 1941, are the drug most generally used today. Regular treatment for 2 to 6 years is required.(6) (20) Nevertheless, sulfones are not effective in stopping deformities once the bones are involved, even with only minimal lesions. Early detection and treatment is important.

The ultimate aim of a system for control of leprosy is to eliminate the bases for transmission through improvement of living conditions and extended systems of hygiene and public health. Such improvement has been accompanied by decrease in prevalence of leprosy.(17) (25) In the meantime, awaiting further development of vaccines or chemo-prophylaxis, the immediately feasible procedures are those which screen the population for cases, screen the patients again for the lepromatous cases, and provide treatment appropriate to each specific case.

THE ORGANIZATIONAL APPROACH IN THE CONTROL OF LEPROSY

For centuries no cure for leprosy existed. Little quantitative data on prevalence were available, only the knowledge that needs were great enough everywhere to overwhelm medical and charitable resources devoted to relief of suffering. Historically, Christian morality, which tends to be individual rather than statistical, had offered demonstrations of concern for the patients, but was limited to custodial care of crippled cases and an attempt to segregate from the rest of society those feared to be contagious. With increased medical knowledge, these charitable institutions have formed the basis for a broader service. Modern efforts are of such a magnitude that their contributions are more than exemplary. With effective therapy at hand it is meaningful to think in terms of organized systems for widespread control. The present problem is to develop systems in such a way that most effective use is made of still limited medical and paramedical resources, to bring the maximum number of cases under control. In many countries such organization exists on a national scale, often with co-ordinative assistance of the World Health Organization. Patterns of clinic organization have been developed, with medical teams traveling paths which radiate from hospital centers to hold carefully timed clinic sessions. The normal evolution of this form of organization has led to some very effective systems.

For purposes of discussion, we regard as the system for control of leprosy all segments of human endeavor which are focused on control of this disease—the medical centers and public health programs, the clinics in the field, the researchers and drug manufacturers. The central actions of the system concerning control of disease are the screening and diagnosis of patients, the administration of out-patient therapy and the provision of in-patient care and rehabilitative care where necessary.

SCREENING AND DIAGNOSIS

Screening and diagnosis are essentially problems of search, often approached by the management scientist with an aim of making best use of resources available for the task. The search process in the problem at hand is to screen the total population for those with symptoms, and to diagnose the lepromatous cases among them.(23)

The diagnostic procedure for lepromatous leprosy is a time-consuming microscopic examination of smears taken from various sites on the patient's body. In current practice, the number of smears examined may range from one to fifteen,(22) consuming physician or technician's time ranging from a few minutes to almost an hour.

An approach to diagnostic problems has been proposed by Blumberg.(3) An applied diagnostic procedure results in a decision of positive or negative findings, and either finding may be true or false. A procedure applied to a given population has empirically determinable probabilities of true positive, true negative, false positive or false negative findings. To each of the four alternatives some value to the patient or society can be attributed, a positive value in the case of true findings, a negative value to false findings. If it is possible to assign such values to these outcomes, alternative procedures may be compared, for the value of a diagnostic procedure may be expressed as the sum of the values of its four possible outcomes weighted by their relative frequencies.

It is at this point that the considerations of an emerging society introduce additional constraints. If it is implied that a developing country is taxing the capacity of its resources—that demands everywhere exceed resources—we must introduce an opportunity cost into alternative courses of action. To estimate the value of a diagnostic procedure, a fifth cost term must be introduced; that is the cost to society of not using a less time-consuming procedure. If the objective of a mass screening program is to detect true positive cases at a maximum rate with a limited set of resources, and if in a disease control program the assumption can be made that the positive finding missed in diagnosis is no more or less harmful to society than that lost because of no diagnosis at all, the problem reduces to a manageable basis. It becomes a matter of choosing the test which maximizes the rate of detection of positive cases.

The following analysis is based on data taken from observations of patients in the leprosarium in Yonda, Coquilhatville, the Congo, in 1958,(22) and from time studies of microscopic examinations in the Leonard Wood Memorial Laboratory at the School of Hygiene and

Public Health at the Johns Hopkins University. An assumption of 10 per cent lepromatous cases in a group of patients is made for discussion of a hypothetical situation.

In the Yonda study, 1301 positive smears were detected by microscopic examination of three smears. Of the total, 82 per cent would have been detected by examination of a single smear taken from an ear lobe, and 98 per cent would have been detected by examination of a pair of smears taken from an ear lobe and skin lesion. The sites for single and double smears noted above were empirically the best of their respective numbers.

In some observations and time study of slide preparation and examination under ideal laboratory conditions, an average time of $2\frac{1}{2}$ minutes was spent in viewing fifty fields in a typical negative slide.* Another half minute was used in placing a slide and approximately $1\frac{1}{2}$ minutes per slide in staining, depending on the number processed simultaneously. These working times are probably shorter than would be encountered under less favorable conditions.

Assuming that the procedures described were applied to a group of patients, of whom 10 per cent would be diagnosed as lepromatous by a three-smear test, it is possible to estimate the rate of diagnosis per personnel hour for one-, two-, and three-smear tests. This is summarized in Table 1, which indicates that the single-smear test is relatively best in that it would produce the greatest number of both true positive and negative diagnoses.† It should be noted that this conclusion is sensitive to variations in the magnitude of personnel time required to take smears and prepare slides. However, a very large increase in such time over that used in these calculations would have been required to alter the conclusions.

Several points should be noted. The conclusion that the one-smear test is categorically best holds only with validity of the

---

*Procedures for searching for possible microscopic particles in a smear is in itself a search problem bearing strong resemblance to those abstracted by Koopman (18) from military mission of searching for a submarine in the sea.

† Ideally these results should be compared with the most exhaustive known, particularly for valid estimates of per cent positives detected.

assumption that the system is more or less indifferent to the false-negative finding. That is to say, if society and the patient are not harmed by the failure to detect a contagious case. The tentative justification for this, even for purpose of discussion, rests in the fact that such cases remain under treatment and are subject to routine re-examination. Deeper knowledge of transmissivity is necessary to assess the problem of diagnosis and out-patient care of lepromatous cases.

TABLE 1

Test	Per cent positives detected	Rate of diagnosis (per personnel hour worked)				
		Examinations	True positives	True negatives	False negatives	False positives
One smear	0·82	13·3	1·09	12·0	0·24	0
Two smears	0·98	8·6	0·84	7·74	0·02	0
Three smears	100	6·3	0·63	5·67	00	0

Routine microscopic procedure calls for examination of fifty fields in a smear. This number is itself subject to optimization as a function of the distribution of bacilli density among smears in a population under mass survey.(15) It is the subject of continuing investigation.

The foregoing analysis is presented not for the intrinsic value of its specific numbers but as a method of approach. As stated, the problem is to make the best use of limited resources. The analysis lends itself readily to a more aggressive application; that is, computation of resources needed if given a set of objectives in terms of number of patients to be screened and treated.

THE ORGANIZATION OF SERVICES FOR DIAGNOSIS AND THERAPY

With the development of effective therapy, with broadened knowledge and diminishing fear of leprosy, with aggressive, universal concern for the health of mankind evidenced by the creation and growth of the World Health Organization, many changes in attitudes and approaches to control of the disease have taken place. The traditional attempts to segregate all patients with manifest symptoms of leprosy have given way to a more enlightened classification of patients and rendering of therapy according to need, and according to the feasibility of integration with other health services. As has been stated, a majority of patients with symptoms of leprosy are not capable of transmitting the disease and are not disabled. They may be treated as out-patients, those who come to the medical service for treatment but do not remain there.

In urban areas—and here we speak of the "developed" countries—out-patient services are frequently an important segment of the work of modern hospitals. In industrialized areas with population heavily concentrated near medical centers, patients come to the hospital, often in such numbers that the administrative procedures of clinic operation become matters of great importance. Operations research in these areas has attempted to develop control of the movement of patients through clinics to reduce delay and discomfort and to divide the services so as to unburden professional staff of non-professional duties. This research(10) (28) may be directly applicable to out-patient leprosy control in urbanized regions.

It is also typical that the disease exists in rural areas and villages far from the main medical centers. This has resulted in the development of traveling clinics in a variety of forms. The particular forms which have evolved have been influenced by geographical and populational characteristics, existing laws, transportation systems, and location of main medical centers. Some idea of the variety of these systems in practice is given by Hemerijckx,(16) who describes in some detail his own activities at Polambakkam, India.

The Leprosy Center at Polambakkam, developed under the auspices of the Fondation Belge contre la Lèpre, was opened in July 1955 to serve an area of about 800 square miles with a population of 388,000. Mobile units to travel among villages were organized. In the beginning, only 176 patients were known, some clinics having as few as five to eight attendants. Four months later the same clinics had over 700 patients. By 18 months, 9591 patients had been treated. By April 1961, 20,017 had received treatment and of them 14,852 were current cases.

The area contains seventy-five villages, most of them served by roads, some of which may not be usable throughout a whole year. Forty-five villages on cross-roads have been selected as clinic sites in an effort to hold patient travel to no more than 6 miles per visit. The number of patients per clinic ranges from 64 to 1004. The clinic may be held in a house, or perhaps under a tree; at any rate, no capital investment or permanent commitment is involved. Weekly clinics are staffed by paramedical workers, who live most often in a subcenter, traveling the circuits by bicycle or motor-cycle. A physician attends the clinic each month. In addition to personnel in the main center, the out-patient work is carried out by two physicians and thirty-two paramedical workers.

An important management aspect is that travel time of staff is lost time, and may be large relative to treatment time. Another matter is the importance of scheduling and reliability in clinic sessions, since patient absenteeism is a problem which may be aggravated by irregularity in clinic schedule. The reader from the management sciences will recognize some familiar problems of routing and scheduling in this system. The determination of minimum travel distance and economic mode of transportation are components of clinic planning. The approach to finding the shortest total lengths of a series of links forming a set of points, known as the "traveling salesman problem", is discussed by Flood[11] and Croes.[5] The challenge here to management science lies not only in technical complexities of the problem, but in the attempt to better a system empirically evolved with skill and wisdom.

IN-PATIENT CARE AND REHABILITATION

Though many leprosy patients may be treated as out-patients, some are or should be hospitalized. Surgical and physiotherapeutic treatment for ulcers and deformities, adverse reaction to drugs, need for custodial care or social pressures call for temporary institutional care. Many leprosaria in existence were built decades ago, when segregation was considered necessary and when—not unrelatedly—prevalence was underestimated. In these institutions the gamut of human needs had to be met, ranging from new admissions with early symptoms to the "burnt-out case", crippled or blind and no longer infectious.

The current views, expressed by WHO,(29) are to provide a set of hospital facilities designed to the specific level of need, integrated where feasible with other health services, and administered in the light of modern knowledge of the disease. It is of historical interest to note that the decline of leprosy in Europe accompanied generally improved living conditions, and that in fact some of the system of general hospitals grew on the physical sites of the obsolete leprosaria.

The evolution of services in the Congo up to 1960 categorized patients and cared for them in the following ways:

Lepromatous cases—Hospitalization encouraged, but the decision of treatment as in-patient or out-patient left to the physician who weighed medical and social factors as well as the availability of facilities.

Crippled patients—Custodial care at governmental expense was available.

Special cases—Those needing intensive or highly specialized care for short periods, e.g. surgery, physiotherapy or complication due to other disease. Selected institutions were equipped and staffed for this purpose.

By careful definition of criteria for admission and discharge and by flexibility in the use of basically sufficient facilities, in-patient problems have been handled adequately. In other areas of the world, the proper balance among facilities has not been achieved; crippled and other chronic leprosy cases have pre-empted facilities from patients who would benefit from short- or long-term hospitalization.

The concept of graduated leprosy services differs little from that of present planners of health services in developed areas of the world. Here also the concept of comprehensive services, categorized according to level of need in contrast to clinical disease, is receiving much attention. Facilities for graduated or "progressive" care(14) (8) are analogous to the levels of intensity of illness in leprosy. In England and America there has been application of queuing theory and statistical techniques to estimation of bed needs for various services as a function of the patterns of occurrence of need and duration of stay.(2) (9) There is no apparent obstacle to direct use of these approaches in the emerging countries. They require definitions of categories of need, workable systems of classification of patients into these categories, and criteria for admission and discharge. They also require statistical knowledge of the population of the region served and a statement of objectives of the health service system, hopefully in quantitative terms. It is perhaps in this philosophy of approach as much as in specific analytic techniques that the management sciences may aid health services everywhere.

CONCLUSION

In the health services, the distinction between developed and emerging countries at the planning level is by no means as sharp as in commerce and industry. Health services in most industrialized countries are themselves in a period of development and change. The task here is less one of transplanting some existing aspect of one society into another than it is of examining an area of human existence which is in rapid development everywhere.

The traditional approaches of public health administration, with multidiscipline attacks on broad system problems, is not radically different from operations research approaches to industrial and military management. This being the case, the management scientist should find in the health services of the world not only a fertile field for his talents, but a set of potential colleagues receptive to his ideas.

ACKNOWLEDGMENTS

The preparation and presentation of this paper has been supported in part by U.S. Public Health Service Research Grant W-167, "Statistical Patterns of Demand for Hospital Services", and by the Johns Hopkins University.

BIBLIOGRAPHY

1. ANVERSOIS, L., News item, *Int. J. Leprosy*, **8,** 233 (1940).
2. BAILEY, N. T. J. "Statistics in Hospital Planning and Design, Applied Statistics." *Journal of the Royal Statistical Society*, **5,** No. 2 (1956).
3. BLUMBERG, M. S. "Evaluating Health Screening Procedures." *Operations Research*, **5,** 3, 319–50, (June 1957).
4. CHENEVEAU, R. "La lutte contre la lèpre en A.E.F." *Med. Afr. noire*, **5,** 535–8 (1958).
5. CROES, G. A. "A Method for Solving Traveling Salesman Problems", *Operations Research*, **6,** 6, 791–812 (Nov. 1958).
6. ERICKSON, P. T. "The Treatment of Leprosy", *Ann. N.Y. Acad. Sci.* **54,** 115–25 (1951).
7. FADDA, S. "La lebbra nelle nostre colonie e nell'Ethiopia", *G. Med. milit.* **84,** 106 (1936).
8. FLAGLE, C. D. "The Problems of Organization for Hospital Inpatient Care", *Proceedings of the Sixth Annual International Meeting of the Institute of Management Sciences* (Pergamon Press, London, 1960).
9. FLAGLE, C. D., LOCKWARD, H., MOSS, J. and STRACHAN, J. *Estimating Bed Needs in a Progressive Care Hospital* (U.S. Public Health Service, Division of Hospital and Medical Facilities, Washington).
10. FLAGLE, C. D., GABRIELSON, I. W., SORIANO, A. and TAYLOR, M. *Analysis of Congestion in an Outpatient Clinic*, Final Report, USPHS Research Grant W-98.
11. FLOOD, M. M. "The Traveling Salesman Problem", *Operations Research*, **4,** 61–75 (Feb. 1956).
12. GAY PRIETO, J. *The WHO Prevalence Surveys*, Symposium on Research in Leprosy; Leonard Wood Memorial and Johns Hopkins University, School of Hygiene and Public Health; Baltimore, 1961.

13. GUINTO, R. S. "Registered Cases of Leprosy and Rates per 1000 Population, with Estimated Total Numbers where available, as Reported by Governments to the Leonard Wood Memorial or to the World Health Organization", *Leprosy Briefs*, **12**, 33–6 and 40 (1961).

14. HALDEMAN, J. C. and ABDELLAH, F. "Concepts of Progressive Patient Care." *Hospitals, J.A.H.A.*, 33 (May 16 and June 1).

15. HANKS, J. H. "Quantitative Aspects of Sampling Leprosy Skin Lesion by the Scraped Incision Method", *Int. J. Leprosy*, **24**, 424–33 (1956).

16. HEMERIJCKX, F. *Rapport sur les activités 1955–1958 du Centre Belge contre la Lèpre à Pollambakkam.*

17. JEANSELME, E. *La Lèpre* (Douin, ed.; Paris, 1934).

18. KOOPMAN, B. O. "The Theory of Search. Part II, Target Detection", *Operations Research*, **4**, 5 (Oct. 1956).

19. LECHAT, M. F. *Bone Lesions in Leprosy*, Symposium on Research in Leprosy; Leonard Wood Memorial and Johns Hopkins University, School of Hygiene and Public Health; Baltimore, 1961.

20. LECHAT, M. F. "L'évolution de la bactérioscopie chez les lépreux traités par les sulfones. I. Délai de négativation", *Ann. Soc. Belge Méd. Trop.* **41**, 509–22 (1961).

21. LECHAT, M. F. *Étude des Mutilations Lépreuses* (Arscia, Bruxelles, and Masson, Paris, coedit., 1961).

22. LECHAT, M. F. "L'évolution de la bactérioscopie chez les lépreux traités par les sulfones. II. Stratégie de l'examen bactérioscopique multiple", *Ann. Soc. Belge Méd. Trop.* **41**, 523–34 (1961).

23. LECHAT, M. F. "Diagnostic des macules lepreuses et plus particulièrement des lésions tuberculoïdes et border-line", *Bull. Inform. Lèpre*, **6**, 36–60 (1958).

24. LECHAT, M. F. and PUISSANT, F. "Problems of Rehabilitation of the Leprosy Patient in a High Prevalence Area of Africa", *J. Chron. Dis.* **13**, 221–7 (1961).

25. RICHARDS, P. "Leprosy in Scandinavia. A Discussion of its Origins, its Survival and its Effects on Scandinavian Life over the Course of Nine Centuries", *Medicinhistorick Arsbok; Stockholm*, 1960.

26. RICHET, P. "Mass Anti-Leprosy Campaigns in French Africa", *Transaction of the VIIth International Congress of Leprology*, Tokyo (Tofu Kyokai ed.) (1958), 414.

27. SHALLER, K. F. "Zur Epidemiologie der Lepra in Äthiopien", *Z. Tropenmed. Parasit.* **10**, 79–94 (1959).

28. SORIANO, A. *A Comparitive Study of Block and Individual Appointment Systems in the Outpatient Department, Wilmer Ophthalmological Clinic*, Report, USPHS Research Grant W-167.

29. WHO-CCTA. *Rapport de la Conférence sur la Lèpre en Afrique*, Technical report (Brazzaville, 1959).

30. CONGO BELGE. *Rapport Annuel de la Direction Générale des Services Médicaux* (Léopoldville, 1953).

PART THREE

CASE EXPERIMENTS AND APPLICATIONS

10

PRACTICAL IMPLEMENTATION OF MANAGEMENT SCIENCES IN INDUSTRIALLY DEVELOPING COUNTRIES

SEBASTIAN B. LITTAUER

Professor and Chairman, Department of Industrial and Management Engineering, Columbia University

IT SEEMS to be common experience that the best laid plans for economic growth do not come to fruition as rapidly or as effectively in industrially developing countries as the "foreign experts" who conceived these plans had hoped for. It may serve a useful purpose to seek the causes of obstruction so that they may be prevented from developing and to look briefly at possible avenues of practical activities which can increase industrial effectiveness.

To begin with we may classify the countries into two categories (whose dividing line may not always be obvious). There are the countries with a negligible amount of industry; and there are a number of countries whose industry is functioning, but far from its full potential. The range of problems confronting these two groups do overlap but the major emphasis differs. In the first group some of the elementary aspects of production know-how may be lacking and personnel competent to give training and training facilities may be quite inadequate. Lack of industry may be owing to lack of resources which cannot be made available even were the industrial know-how there. It is obvious that under such circumstances the implementation of the management sciences most commonly appearing in the literature are not likely to be readily put into practice and in consequence are not likely to be fruitful no matter how diligently and sincerely their implementation is attempted. In these situations basic economic inquiry and over-all planning is in order. The management sciences needed are not those designed for directly increasing productive effectiveness or for developing management skill in decision-making. The problems are more basic, more difficult, and perhaps without answers in the sense of modern industrial society. We shall not attempt to delineate an approach to implementing management sciences under these circumstances. The requirements under these circumstances are related to resource development, to industry selection and to inculcating basic operative skills rather than to competence intrinsic in management sciences.

In countries where there exist industries of some importance but where the need both for industrial expansion to, say, two to three times the existing output, where productivity can be increased by some 50 to 100 per cent, and where the key to these contributions is in the hands of management, there management sciences can be implemented with a high probability of success and in reasonably quick order. To be sure there are attendant social, political and broad economic problems which work counter to the promotion of productivity, gross production and economic growth, yet considerable net advances accrue. We cannot go into these ramifications of industrial development nor are we competent to do so. We have, however, observed definite genuine advances in widely separated countries which are markedly different in size, resources, cultural characteristics, climate, and degrees of industrial development. Our work made evident to us a large variety of mundane practical problems as well as the broad general problems requiring more patient treatment. We have seen how progress can be made in little ways and how management can be influenced by so-called "indoctrination" programs. The progress in managerial sophistication is slow, but definite and persistent when continuing effort is applied.

Perhaps our discussion so far can be summed up briefly as follows: practical fruitful results follow when specific needs of the country are permitted to guide the implementation of management sciences. Three avenues of approach may be taken simultaneously:

1. *Short Range.* Introduction of simple work-a-day techniques in work measurement, statistical quality control, and inventory control in individual plants.

2. *Intermediate Range.* Introduction of in-plant training, industrial institute organization, industrial institute programs, engineering school programs, intermediate level management training programs, publications.

3. *Long Range.* Introduction of professional societies and journals, regional planning, government development programs, and government planning groups.

In countries where, however, the major problems are those of: Where are the basic resources? what industries are needed? how to establish a labor supply? and how inculcate simple productive know-how and the like, the setting is not yet ready for those aspects of the management sciences which can most readily pay dividends and in which there exists adequate experience. Ironically enough both more primitive programs are needed as well as more profound and larger-scale investigations. Management cannot become more scientific and more sophisticated because there are no enterprises to manage and no managers to indoctrinate. Hence many fruitless and frustrating experiences in promulgating the management sciences can be avoided by saving the efforts of the scholars of management science for countries in the second countries. The discussion following will be drawn from the writer's experience in three countries in three different continents.

One of these countries is scientifically sophisticated, industrially developed in some regions, and has a great cultural tradition. Yet a great part of this country is still practically underdeveloped industrially and some 10 years ago, when the establishment of sophisticated production procedures and managerial methods was formally

N

undertaken, the country was naïve in management practice. The country had (and, of course, still has) many persons possessed of considerable technical and scientific training. While these persons —the young in particular—were quite amenable to the advent of modern managerial and industrial productive practices, they were more naturally inclined to linear algebras than programming scarce resources, to probability and mathematical statistics than to production control and statistical quality control, to individual skill in individually controlled workmanship than to skilful managerially controlled mass-production procedures, and in general to formal analysis rather than to experimentalist investigation. In short, the cultural tradition was rationalist and this presented a cultural problem to those undertaking management science indoctrination.

The program was directed principally at the intermediate range with some effort devoted to attaining some of the short-range objectives and to establishing the ground work for long-range planning. The initial program was specifically devoted to industrial quality control and principally to training. Two intensive courses were provided in two principal centers, with attendance well over one hundred professional persons in each. The composition of the enrollees consisted largely of engineers, with, however, a substantial representation of college teachers, production supervisors, training personnel, and plant executives. While the material presented consisted essentially of a unified coverage of industrial statistical quality control methods and techniques, the presentation was not strictly formal and there were notable digressions. In the first place the SQC practices were motivated by actual problems offered by enrollees. So far as possible some substantial attack on such problems was made and in many cases practical results were obtained. Then there were problem working sessions. And, of considerable importance, there were lengthy sessions during which enrollees raised questions of a specifically practical nature about problems existing in their own organizations. Fortunately, many practical answers were given and thus provided useful quick results. Hence one can say that this intermediate-range program provided a basis for eventually implementing a phase of management science practice and for perpetuating future practice by indoctrinating plant executives, training personnel, personnel responsible for industrial training and teachers of engineering.

The winning over of many plant executives was important because these men were the key to whether or not certain special practices would be directly introduced and whether or not further encouragement would be given to the management sciences. The stimulus to engineering teachers had, of course, a long-range effect as well, providing the basis for future engineers with competence in phases of the management sciences. And further, there was a nucleus of plant production personnel schooled in techniques which they could put into practice, together with a body of design and development engineers cognizant of the management sciences as contributing to the effectiveness of their work as professional engineers.

The effects if this program might not have been lasting if it were not for a number of other aspects, some stemming directly from the core program. In the first place, the perspective of management science and operations research was discussed both formally with the whole group and informally with individuals seeking further insight. Questions of organization and of how and where to start implementing management sciences in general were raised alongside discussion on statistical quality control in particular. In fact, the interest and enthusiasm for management sciences and operations research seemed to be engendered by development of a particular discipline and set of techniques. These intimate sessions were essentially consulting sessions, sometimes associated with plant visits. Hence, aspects of everyday practice were introduced in association with the longer-range technical training so as to tie down the hope for longer-range effect with a more immediately realizable practical result.

An interesting part of this program, and an innovation for that country, was a round of plant visits by all the enrollees. The encouragement of exchange of know-how and possible mutual assistance (even by competitors) helped eliminate the tradition of "secret trade practice" and promote the perspective of scientific practice which can be learned and shared.

The educational developments were promoted not only by reaching university teachers and plant training personnel but also by getting support from organizations of industrialists as well as civic productivity institutes for local training programs. Together with industrial and professional societies which were set up as a result of this program the support for training in the management sciences, engendered by the attack on economic control of industrial production, was sufficiently strong and on a sufficiently broad front to ensure an enduring pursuit of scientific method in the management of industrial production.

One other phase of the approach made in the program described helped insure its effectiveness. One-day conferences were held especially for top executives in five different cities. The response from this level provided support for training in the plant, in industrial institutes, and in the engineering schools. Top executive support also helped in the start of the professional societies and journals. This is the only aspect of long-range planning that we participated in in this program. The other aspects of the long-range phase of implementing management sciences are going apace, but we have no direct knowledge of its effect and of its co-ordination with this program. We do know, however, that there is regional planning and that there is a quasi-governmental industrial complex which is not only implementing management sciences, but also providing a comprehensive university level school of management and supporting an excellent journal devoted to the field of management.

There are a number of cases that could be reported on to show how both the pursuit of and the practices of various aspects of management sciences have progressed. It is sufficient to state that the management sciences are now taken for granted in the business and industrial life of this country; they are taught in the engineering and business schools and in special professional schools; there are active and progressive professional societies promoting the management sciences; and the government is cognizant of the possible value of these disciplines in its military and civic planning. It is not intended to make this look like a success story. The contrast between present practices and those of 10 years ago is marked, and principally by the fact that the country under consideration does not need to look to "experts from abroad" to guide it in the management of its enterprises. The interesting feature is that *there has been practical, fruitful implementation of management sciences by a three-pronged humble approach of just trying to do things, things with possible immediate pay-off together with things that have a more enduring value.* Furthermore, these accomplishments did not result from "global" planning, preparing reports and trying to encompass the whole economy in one plan. And, it is emphasized again, developments such as occurred in this country could never have occurred in truly underdeveloped countries. Some old-fashioned common sense is needed in order to determine where to direct one's efforts.

Another country to which this general approach has been applied is much smaller than country A, had much less industrial development, had much less managerial know-how, much less of natural resources, and in general much less favorable conditions for industrial development. But, in spite of those handicaps, country B had (and still has) one major asset, namely the will to survive and the will to work and the brain power to be chaneled. Efforts in this country were not as well organized as in country B, yet persistent application to practical problems and to indoctrination has brought some genuine practical results. As in country A, the intellectual tradition leaned toward formalism and ironically significant scientific discoveries were not uncommon whereas industrial and management progress were naïve. Yet here was a people lifting themselves economically largely by their boot straps. This effort was not enough to provide for national needs, in spite of the fact that agricultural developments were substantially reducing dependence on imports of food supplies. The seeming more rapid development in agriculture may appear at first to be paradoxical, but the explanation is rather simple. The agricultural insufficiency was not owing to lack of management skill but to basic problems of soil, fertilizer, rainfall and other indigenously scientific agricultural problems. Scientific research provided the people with answers as to what to plant and where, how to get going and how to nurture. With such knowledge applied to long-neglected land the progress was remarkable. And the example of this country B is a strong case in point for the caution necessary in undertaking the salvation of so-called underdeveloped countries. Industrial practice is relatively modern and sophisticated, whereas agriculture is as old as the hills and can be stimulated by even humble application of know-how without building large plants and introducing elaborate managerial controls. While such agricultural development is not comparable in productivity to that of the modern mass-industrialized ranch-farms of the United States, the conversion of relatively unproductive lands to regular production feeds a people and is hailed as a miracle.

The lot of industry is quite different. Much of the scientific and technical knowledge can be there and yet satisfactory and economic production does not result because worker skill is not developed and there is little tradition of managerial know-how, not to speak of awareness of the range of management sciences. In country B there is considerable need for implementation of aspects of the management sciences, principally day-to-day control techniques in production.

Conscious implementation of a nation-wide management program was initiated by a quasi-government corporation—essentially privately managed but deriving considerable government financial support. That this complex of some twenty industrial units was functioning was a testimony to the enterprise of certain vigorous leaders. That these industries provided much valuable industrial output was saliently true. But by butter and egg accounting analysis a number of the companies in the complex were not making money and this state of affairs did not augur well for the country's necessary economic growth, for their acquiring much-needed foreign currency. An inquiry into the companies' productive effectiveness was asked for.

The attempt to implement management sciences here was played by ear. It is not necessary to go into the whole program and detail the results. The basic point of this discussion, namely, the simple three-pronged approach to getting some practical applications going, to get in-plant training going, to indoctrinate intermediate management, to introduce university courses and to get management consciousness of the need for the management sciences was undertaken over a period of years. Eventually a professional society was organized as well as an upper management association. Many companies are using analytical techniques in work measurement, developing statistical control programs, instituting analytical inventory decision procedures, programming methods and queueing techniques to considerable advantage. These developments were not the result of over-all "scientific" promulgation of a management science economic development program. They came as a result of undertaking, wherever the opportunity presented itself, one or another of the practical applications of the managerial control techniques to industrial production. Training went apace with this slowly mushrooming of practice. This development of implementation of management sciences was helped considerably by the presence among the country's engineers, managers, consultants and engineering teachers of a few highly competent persons who on their own were putting into operation their management science skills. These persons were helped by the "foreign experts" and in turn did considerable to bolster all the efforts that were being made to make industrial functioning more effective. In a small country such as this one a half-dozen dynamic sophisticated figures can have a significant influence on its industrial development, especially when buttressed by some outside help.

Over a period of almost 10 years there has been a considerable growth in the implementation of management science practices. There has been a measureable increase in productivity as well as improvement in industrial relations. Industry has taken on the complexion of effective mass-production. Management has become more sophisticated, but has yet a long way to go. There has been little long-range development except for: (1) general support by the government of management development programs, and (2) strong application of encouragement by the military of management science and operations research. The actual accomplishments in country B are not yet so significant as in country A, but there has been established a very important training and education program which is nation-wide. There is much in-plant training, there are various "extension" courses sponsored by a Productivity Institute, conferences sponsored by a Management Association, and what may have the most lasting and fruitful effect, a fully developed and well-rounded university program in industrial engineering, management sciences, and operations research. The curriculum for both the undergraduate degree in industrial engineering and the M.S. degree with major in management science and operations research are as sound and well balanced as any college curricula with which this writer is familiar.

It seems that now there is in country B a well-rounded and reasonably widely implemented management science activity. This was made possible not by attempting a "global" management science plan for the country but by repeated and extensive application of particular practices over the whole gamut of short, intermediate and longe-range management science planning.

The third country differed from the other two in that its population was about one-half that of the greater, its culture was rather high, mixed, and yet a great extent of the country was quite underdeveloped. While the country had more extensive and higher development of industry in certain concentrations than existed in the smaller country just discussed, it was nowhere near as highly developed as the first country that was discussed. One might say of this country that it was of a different cultural and industrial complexion than were the other two countries. Furthermore, this country had rather great natural resources useful in industry, as well as considerable agricultural resources. It had some large government-operated utility complexes, yet there was a lack of managerial outlook and know-how. Most of the privately controlled industries were operated by families where the directorship was inherited. There were, of course, a number of industrial operations under foreign control which to some extent partook of the methods of modern management science. There was considerable evidence of worker ability where training opportunities were afforded and where good managerial control was in effect. There was no question but that the people had the potential for highly efficient modern mass-production. But in general throughout the country managerial effort was relatively unsophisticated.

At the time the group with which this writer was connected came to this country, there had been already instituted in the larger cities some degree of work measurement and other of the classical factory techniques which were supposed to bring about economy of production. There were some courses in trade schools, and in one of the universities in elements of Industrial Engineering and Industrial Economics. But in general there was no tradition of Industrial Engineering or Management Science or Operations Research in the universities. There was, of course, a high level of scholarship among the faculty members, but this was limited to the "pure" intellectual activity. The writer's group was called upon to attack some of the problems of a large governmental producing and distributing activity, which appeared to be operating well technically but inefficiently economically. The main focus of attack of our group was on the inventory policy. The original intention was to establish corporate wide managerial controls which it was believed would both raise the effectiveness of production *per se* and reduce the incidents of imbalance and excessive cost of maintaining inventory. But under the circumstances, it was imposed upon the group to examine the inventory situation. This afforded, however, considerable opportunity for implementing principles of management science and effecting economy.

In this situation the group could not operate as it felt was most advisable nor in the spirit outlined at the beginning of the article. It was hoped, however, that a good start could be made in making one aspect of the company's operation reasonably sound. Fortunately, before attacking the inventory problem by so-called mathematical models, we were able to attack the whole purchasing problem and set that in order. This in itself had the effect of providing a considerable economy in the utilization of the staff of the company and in effecting considerable simplification in maintaining inventory, which in itself led to economy in the total volume of inventories on hand. While no formal training program was submitted in this case, in the day-to-day job of getting the information necessary to evolve a satisfactory inventory policy it was possible to indoctrinate those members of the company who assisted us, in some fundamental elements of inventory policy decision-making.

The culmination of efforts in this program was a rather sound fundamentally simple inventory plan. The plan was presented and explained to and discussed with the appropriate officials for a sufficient period of time before our group was obliged to leave. We would like to say that we accomplished something quite positive here, had indoctrinated the group in some modern management science methodology and had produced something of considerable economic value to a large company. It turned out, however, that no one in the officialdom understood anything about the plan and only one of the engineers who worked with us was capable of understanding its pro-bablistic aspects and its economic importance. He was given the job by the director to study and digest the plan and make recommenda-tions. While this young engineer did get to thoroughly understand the inventory policy and to appreciate how it might be implemented in this co-operation, he was unable to move officialdom to any practical application. I can say that it is now a number of years, and nothing has been done about implementing this policy. The only saving grace of this job is that the new purchasing procedure was put into effect with a considerable saving of the time required to process purchase orders and, in the course of doing so, effecting considerable economy. There is one comic aspect of this heroic attempt to implement the management sciences in a country where they could do a considerable amount of good, and one ironic con-sequence. In the early part of the project a number of representa-tives of the management and of the local consulting firms were very much enthused by the prospect of getting a large-scale digital com-puter at an expenditure of between 1 million and 2 million dollars.

This proposal was vetoed by the American consultant and as yet the company does not have a computer. But the fact of the matter is that the company had made no attempt to implement policy for which they would invest such a large sum of money. Here is a very good example of the attempts to do something on a grand scale when those for whom the effort is undertaken are not quite ready to walk. And ironically enough the only engineer of the company staff who had the background of necessary disciplines and the initiative and energy to prepare himself adequately for implementing the inventory policy developed, together with other aspects of management science, left the company to join a new group of young men who organized as consultants in Operations Research and the Management Sciences. We believe that the climate was not prepared for the introduction of large-scale management projects and that this project could have fared much better if appropriate training was made available.

Fortunately for the progress of industry in this country there existed other avenues of effort. In the first place, under the auspices of the ILO, there had been established productivity institutes under the direction of people who have had experience in the operating of such productivity institutes in countries with about the same level of industrial know-how. Their simple undertakings are developing rather well and are yielding some practical results in particular industrial situations. There are United States commissions which are providing analysis of the industrial situation and offering training at levels where the training can be effective. One difficulty is that for a country of the size and population of this one, there is not sufficient co-ordination among the various agencies, both governmental and private, which are attempting to foster industrial development and the implementation of scientific and efficient managerial direction.

There have, however, been further developments. And it seems that these developments are resulting from the education of certain people in the potential of modern scientific method in Industrial Operation and Control. The initiative is being taken by groups of younger men who have had training in modern methods of Industrial

Operations, Operations Research and the Management Sciences. These young men have set about doing jobs for industry on the premise that modern scientific method of Industrial Operation and Management are essential to the country's economic growth and that such endeavor offers considerable opportunity to them as individuals to gain positions of influence and affluence. Efforts to introduce what is hoped to be the most effective means for raising industrial productivity and the standard of living as well as the self-sustaining potential of the country is supported by certain of the forward-looking members of the military hierarchy. In fact, much of the work that has gone on in the government-supported operations has been at the insistence of the military. It is unfortunate that this has sparked efforts on such a scale that practical results were not as readily achieved as the interest and good will of the proponents had hoped for. But this spark on the part of the military is very helpful toward effecting the implementation of modern scientific methods of industrial operations and managerial control.

There have, however, been other developments in this country. At about the time our group left its first project there were established in one of the universities some courses in statistical quality control, probability and statistical method applied to industry, and courses in linear programming. This began a rather organized plan for the development of a course of study in Industrial Engineering, Operations Research and the Management Sciences. Simultaneously there were developed courses in Business Management. Of course, many of these overlap with what is called operations research and the management sciences. Nevertheless, this was all to the good and the shift from concern with economic theory *per se* to concern with more practical considerations related to making business and industry more efficient. The development of this course structure is not primarily a mark of the increasing intellectual development in the country. On the contrary, there is a rather high level of culture, and as was said before, a high level of academic accomplishment. But the new university program was a modern development in that it gave recognition to the fact that intellectual processes could be made practically effective in day-to-day life and that there was such a thing as training for industrial executives and for managerial personnel.

An aftermath of the large-scale program in which this writer participated was an invitation to come back and set up an Operations Research–Management Science training conference for engineers and intermediate management. In spite of many difficulties in setting up this program and the cost involved, it turned out to be very successful. There were some twenty-five enrollees representing some of the most important industries as well as some small enterprises, including one chain retail activity. A 4-week intensive program, including problem sessions, was initiated and was well and enthusiastically attended by the enrollees. While the time allotted was short there was opportunity to develop some of the foundation upon which Operations Research and Management Science rests and to develop certain of the important fundamental techniques. This 1-month session was followed somewhat later by an intensive review session for those of the enrollees who were interested in attending. Of course, this review session was given by the local consulting group. The important part about this program is, not that a certain amount of training was given, but that it initiated a practice in this country which had not been undertaken before that time, namely that of engineers and executives being away from their work for a specified period of time and taking intensive training either in modern ideologies or in refresher material. The aftermath of this program was, fortunately, much healthier than that of the original large-scale inventory study. A number of the firms whose executives had attended this program had undertaken to have training programs presented to their staffs during working hours or at least on time that was paid for by the company. They also invited proposals on certain Operations Research–Management Science projects, some of which have already been implemented. The following year this young consulting group was invited by two of its clients to conduct short intensive training programs in some of the special techniques of management science. This was done successfully, to be sure with some help from this country. Following these intensive programs the group was invited to undertake other projects by their clients. It seems that most of this work in the implementation of the management sciences in these organizations is going on successfully. The conclusion seems to be that it is desirable, if not really necessary, to co-ordinate the implementation of the management sciences with appropriate training programs under the auspices of local groups whether these groups be the industries themselves, consulting groups or university departments. It might also be added at this point that recently the university has expanded its offerings in Industrial Engineering, Operations Research and the Management Sciences to where there is a substantial program leading to the equivalent of our Master's degree and paralleling very closely the educational programs of our best institutions.

A little comment on the attempt to implement the management sciences in this country is in order. The results in this country are not perhaps quite as successful as in the other two countries. There has been some motivation of achievement in the direction of the instituting of actual projects and training executives and getting a university program going. While there has been simultaneous work in the Productivity Institute and at some of the more elementary levels of factory production know-how, we feel that this is one part of the program which is not as highly developed as is desirable. Again, however, the activities in this country give evidence of the fact that the three-pronged program suggested at the beginning of this paper can be effective and that global undertakings may perhaps dissipate energies without attaining fruitful results.

11

OPERATIONS RESEARCH ON THE WAY IN CHINA

J. G. WAARDENBURG

The Hague

INTRODUCTION

THERE are two viewpoints which can make the subject of our paper interesting. On the one hand, until some years ago communist countries did not pay much attention to the application of mathematics to economic management, but this attitude has changed in recent years. It is interesting to see in what degree this change is also taking place in communist China. On the other hand, China is a typical example of an emerging country, although the new régime has done its utmost to promote industrialization, and for this reason the application of O.R. in China is not devoid of interest, especially in the context of studies on applications of management sciences in emerging countries.

As in so many studies about actual China, there are only few accessible sources. In the main Chinese papers, a few scattered articles, some of which were translated into English, have been published (1) and, as far as we know, only one article on this subject was written outside China.(2)

Thus, on account of dearth of information we cannot claim to do justice to our subject, but must restrict ourselves more or less to a series of images and remarks, to which we add some incidental information about points more or less related to the nucleus of our subject. Hereby we will follow closely what is reported, sometimes even giving scope to the Chinese way of expression, leaving most of the interpretation and conclusion to the reader.

THE STORY

The scarcity of information is also due to a no more than about 4 years' application of O.R. in mainland China, to which we will first pay attention. We do know something about the background against which our story is enacted. After a rehabilitation period of 3 years in 1953, the first 5-year plan started with a strong emphasis on heavy industry and the rapid collectivization of agriculture. At the beginning of the second 5-year plan period in 1958 there came the unexpected creation of the communes, with the setting up of much local handicraft industry and the remarkable start of the "Big Leap Forward", with a strong emphasis on extending the quantity of output, surpassing all targets indicated before in the preliminary second 5-year plan and centered around the making of steel. Besides, there came the nation-wide drive to combine education with productive labour. The Big Leap Forward lasted 3 years and although especially in the beginning a remarkable increase of output in several sectors of national economy took place, this increase proved to be too much unbalanced, and after two bad agricultural harvests in 1959 and 1960, serious difficulties and frictions arose, showing the dependence of the economy on agriculture. Since 1961 we have, in industry, no longer found a drive for increasing the output but an emphasis on the quality and variety of products and the lowering of production costs. Agriculture is then taken as "the foundation of economy", beside industry as "the leading factor", and "the whole party and the whole people go in for agriculture in a big way".(3) From the end of 1961 we have found signs of a new reflection on the theory of economic development and unlike at the time of the Big Leap Forward, we now everywhere meet with the following words: smooth, balance, interconnection, proportionate, etc. Thus enough for the background and now for the story.

Although since 1955 some mathematicians have been interested in Operations Research, the initial actual applications date from 1958 and are closely related to the Big Leap Forward. They were especially an outcome of the drive for the combination of education and research with productive labour, when mathematicians went into the fields and factories, and found—to their surprise?—part of their mathematics applicable. The first results were made in 1958 in Shantung Province, which became a kind of pilot region for the application of O.R. and so the nursery of the later movement for applying O.R. nationwide. As these first results in 1958 were only scarce and some opposition was met both from mathematicians and local managers who, as was reported, feared contamination of their mathematics and devaluation of their practical experience,(4) the Party committee of Shantung Province "called a leap forward conference of science and technology workers in July 1959" "in response to the great call of the 8th plenum of the Party for opposing right tendencies and exerting efforts", thus making the application of O.R. a concern of its own. This conference called upon the science and technology workers "to leave their laboratories and class-rooms" and accepted linear programming, to which the application of O.R. had been restricted these first years, as a means of serving economic construction, communications and transport, and people's communes.(5) Then started a mass movement, so typical of modern China, to popularize L.P. all-in with the well-known means of broadcasts, ballad singing to the accompaniment of bamboo clappers, story telling, peep-shows, etc. It has been reported that this movement expanded from 3000 teachers and students of institutes of higher education to 20,000 managers of factories and transport organizations, 100,000 teachers and pupils of secondary and primary schools and 200,000 "positive elements" among the masses of peasants and workers, while 8,000,000 people came in touch with L.P. in one way or another.(6) The total population of Shantung numbers about 50,000,000 people. A report of Ch'ufu Normal College—a college apparently very active in this movement—mentions that by September 1959 its propaganda had reached 1,890,000 persons in Tsining,

O

Linyi and Hotze areas, while 129 training courses had started and 1600 technical persons capable of independently applying L.P. had been trained.(7)

The first and most important results were obtained in the transport sector with rational distribution of commodities, later on in industry, e.g. with rational cutting of rolled steel and steel bars, allocation of equipment and manpower, in agriculture with e.g. rational planning of threshing grounds and irrigation ditches and rational crop-planting.

In May 1960 a provincial on-the-spot conference was held for the purpose of summarizing results, indicating further fields of application such as "summer harvesting, summer sowing and iron and steel production, which tasks were urgent at that time"(8) and further popularizing L.P.

In July the Chinese Academy of Sciences convened a national on-the-spot "Yun Ch'ou Hsueh" (O.R.) conference in Tsinan (Shantung), where twenty-two academic papers on O.R. were read and the experiences of Shantung Province were discussed. One of the presidents of the conference was the well-known Professor Hua Lo-Keng, Director of the Institute of Mathematics of the Chinese Academy of Sciences, who is, moreover, also actively involved in the propagation of O.R. as appears from several articles by his hand.(9) This conference was the sign for a nationwide spread of L.P. and from then several reports tell about movements and application in, for example, the provinces Hopei, Kansu, Hupei Hunan and Chiangsu, where sometimes applications had already been made before. Nevertheless, after March 1961, we can hardly find any explicit report on Yun Ch'ou Hsueh.(10) How has the movement gone on and did mathematics influence the national economic policy? Before we discuss these questions we will turn our attention to several details of the story such as the simplicity of the methods, detailed information about applications and results, difficulties encountered and the fundamental attitude in China towards applications of O.R.

THE METHODS

A remarkable feature of the reports is the claim that L.P. has been popularized. On the one hand, this must have been necessary for any extensive application in view of the relatively small group of available mathematicians and eventual engineers, on the other hand L.P. can be demonstrated relatively simply and the calculations of the simplex method require no more than addition, subtraction, multiplication and division to be used mechanically by hand computation for small problems. Besides, the reports emphasize the necessity of simpler and more pictorial methods, better understandable for the masses and usable for complicated schemes.(11) Thus, for example, a "Graphical Method" is developed for transport problems and the "Graphical Method of Odd and Even Nodes", sometimes combined with little poems or formulae to help memorization.

A. In transportation often two irrational phenomena occur: counter-flow and detour. The following "Graphical Method" has been used to detect and overcome these wastes.(12) The roads of transportation are drawn on a map, with their lengths indicated and the transports are indicated by arrows on the right side. Cross-hauling of empty cars or cars with the same materials are immediately detected (Fig. 1). Detour can be detected by looking at all closed circuits in the scheme and following the rule that the sum of the arrows on either side must be less than the perimeter of the circuit (Figs. 2, 3). The method is said to be as applicable as the tableau method for transportation problems.

B. Another method is the "Graphical Method of Odd and Even Nodes", applicable to the route of a postman, referring to the "Königsberg seven-bridge problem" and based on a simple topological property of networks. To give an example:(13) Starting from A, all points must be visited, afterwards again returning to A (Fig. 4). The odd points in which an odd number of line segments come together are marked, next are linked up in pairs, on condition that the connecting lines don't intersect and that their summed lengths in each closed circuit don't exceed half the perimeter of the circuit. Now the best route doubles only these connecting lines, e.g. A L K B K D E J L H G I G F C A.

C. If in a transportation problem the dispatching points and the roads are fixed, whereas the delivery point is still to be determined, as e.g. when a threshing ground must be located for several not too big wheat fields, the following "formula" is advocated:(14) "the best place is where the quantity of wheat brought in from each road is less than half the total". The threshing ground should be in A.

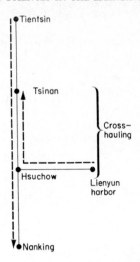

Fig. 1

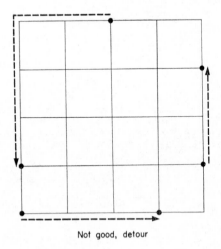

Not good, detour

Fig. 2

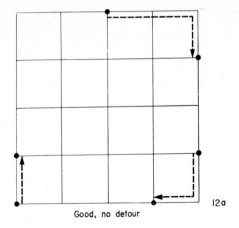

12a

Good, no detour

Fɪɢ. 3

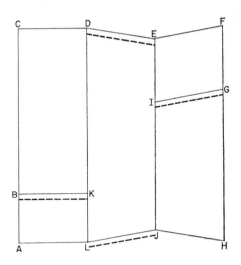

Fɪɢ. 4

D. Another problem arises if only dispatching points have been located, whereas the roads and the delivery points are still to be fixed, e.g. when for several factories with known annual demand for transport in an area, a railway station must be located in such a way as to obtain the minimum total ton-kilometers of freight shipped from and to the station within the area.(15) The following mechanical method is advocated: "Take a piece of cardboard, draw dots on it to represent the positions of the factories, then punch a smooth hole through each of the dots and put a string through each of them. Fasten weights proportionate to the respective transport volumes to the ends of the strings. Then gather the top ends of these strings together and hook them into a small metal ring and hold the ring high above the cardboard. Then let the ring go. The site of the railway station should be where the ring falls under the action of the weighted strings."

More than once the reports warn that these and other methods must be used flexibly, must be slightly adjusted in particular cases, e.g. when the roads have any slope.

In general it may prove more difficult to judge where these methods can be applied and to formulate the model, e.g. before the simplex method can be used, than to compute the results themselves. These judgments and models can be given by the above-mentioned teachers and students of institutes of higher learning and probably "technical persons capable of independently applying L.P."

Another aspect is that it is doubtful whether for problems not suitable for L.P. also simple methods can be devised, such as the mechanical method, mentioned as number four. The desirability of such methods has been talked about with the mathematicians, (16) because several such problems are encountered in the field. For involved methods, not enough personnel is available and one is afraid to "be isolated from the masses". On the other hand, the masses are praised, of course, to be so capable as to apply these methods. As long as such simple methods are not yet devised, mathematicians are studying, and asked to study, the more involved O.R. techniques, such as non-linear programming, dynamic programming, queueing-theory, on which an introductory article appeared in the *People's Daily*(17), etc., and their mathematical foundations. Thus, the development of mathematics is claimed also to have been stimulated.(18) Are there any signs of activities or even results in these fields? First, there are several reports mentioning study of non-linear programming, dynamic programming, theory of matrices, theory of games, network theory, numerical analysis, functional analysis, probability theory and statistics, differential equations, etc., stimulated by the whole movement,(19) during which studies a new respect for the old professor arose.(20) New books were written, e.g. on "Lectures on the Theory of Mathematical Programming" and "Mathematical Statistics and Qualitative Control".(21) Also it has been reported that teaching methods were being improved, drawing the students more actively into the educational process by scientific discussion classes and forums.(22)

Nevertheless, it is difficult to get an idea of the level of these studies. Thus we turn our eye to the scientific literature of the last few years. Mathematics were not well developed in China and mainly theoretically and specialistically directed according to the survey articles of Hua Lo-keng and Marshall H. Stone.(23) During the last few years there has been, quite understandably, a rapid change of interest in favour of applied mathematics and their foundation. East European mathematicians, among whom apparently M. Fisz and K. Urbanik have helped the Chinese with training (e.g. in probability theory) while several Chinese students in mathematics have studied in Russia. Only a small number of the articles in this field are published in English in *Scientia Sinica* and *Science Record* at Peking, some in Russian in Russian journals, while in the summer of 1962 an American translation of the *Acta Mathematica Sinica* will start.(24) We mention with all reservations the results of an incomplete survey of Chinese articles on O.R., automation, numerical mathematics, probability theory and mathematical statistics, since 1958, which have appeared in *Science Record*, *Scientia Sinica* or been mentioned in the *Mathematical Review*: four on Mathematical Statistics, four on Stochastic Processes, ten on Automation and three on Dynamical Systems and two on Information Theory, six on Numerical Mathematics, two on Theory of Games,(25) two on Queueing Theory,(26) and one on Operation of Water Reservoirs.(27)

During a visit to China at the end of 1958 I saw a remarkable example of the heavy emphasis on direct applications of mathematics, viz. that third- and fourth-year mathematical students were competing in building small electronic computers, although there was no sign of immediate use for them.

Nevertheless, there are indications that some time after 1958 it has been understood that a thorough study of pure and advanced mathematics is necessary, also as a condition for a real further development.(28) Before concluding these remarks on method, we must say that on the practical level the real participation of the mathematicians in productive labour in agriculture and factory and their close contacts with the people, normally engaged in that work, have been said to be an essential point in reaching any results.(29) Also close co-ordination between different departments, e.g. those of transportation and distribution of commodities, and centralization and unification are advocated in order to improve O.R. applications, because then the whole interconnection of systems will appear to full advantage.(30)

THE DETAILS OF THE STORY

Turning now to the many examples of successful applications of L.P., we must remark that the Chinese press is in the practice of telling "hero-stories", well-chosen cases being found back again and again. Consequently, these examples do not necessarily represent the whole movement, although they are vouching for it. Moreover, with very few exceptions, all examples date from before April 1961.

Transport

From this sector, which is one of the bottlenecks of the Chinese economy, the most and first applications have been reported. It has been mentioned in several reports that in Shantung the transportation efficiency of the means of long-distance communication increased generally by 10–15 per cent by rational transportation schemes and systematic vehicle distribution based on rational organization of supply, dispatch of carts, loading and unloading, receiving and sending of cars. In detail it has been told that the Tsinan Truck Transport Comp. greatly reduced detours and cross-hauling of empty cars and raised the car loading rate from 71·03 per cent to 82·18 per cent. In 7 months, the turn-round volume of trucks was raised by 7,010,000 ton/km. "According to incomplete figures" in railway transportation throughout Shantung Province, where formerly goods were shipped to the provincial capital before further distribution, which caused great waste, transportation capacity was increased to the extent of 235,610,000 ton/km between January and June 1960. In short-distance transportation the results are said to have been even more marked: the Tsinan Transportation Comp. introduced L.P. and improved management, thus in 6 months raising the actual loading rate for handcarts from 63·73 per cent to 78·04 per cent and turn-round volume by 449,000 ton/km and raising mileage utilization rate for handcarts from 50 per cent to 62·5 per cent or 75 per cent, while shortening workers' working hours by 2–3 hours.(31) Another report has told of a saving of 43·28 million ton/km, equivalent to 904 trucks to handle in 1 month, in 5 months, in Tsinan municipality.(32) In Tientsin (Hopei) municipality mileage utilization rate on the improved transportation line increased from 56 per cent to 70 per cent, and in some cases to 90 per cent; functional hours of truck operation were raised from 40 per cent to 80 per cent.(33)

In Chi-ning, in railway transportation, irrational arrival at the station, irrational use of special lines and confusion in using storage yards, created an enormous storage of 40–50,000 tons of goods was found. Improvement has been made but no figures have been given. The only report published in 1962 states that the Tsining Municipal Transportation Comp. of Shantung Province has "persevered in the employment of L.P." and had the success that thereby the ratio of mileage covered by the carts increased from 50 per cent to 60·1 per cent and the daily output *per capita* from 5·8 ton/km to 7·6 ton/km.(34) A long article appeared in the same journal and on the same day recommending the use of L.P. for short-distance transportation, of which improvement and utmost use has been strongly emphasized by the government since the summer of 1961. In combination with transportation, the rational supply, storage and distribution of goods is advocated and practised.

Industry

In this sector applications of L.P. have been reported in connection with the use of materials, division of tasks among machine tools, distribution and composition of labor power, warehouse layout, continuous operational lines, rational intra-factory transportation, etc. In Tsinan No. 1 Machine Tool Plant, rational cutting of steel raised utilization of rolled steel and steel bars from 96 per cent to 99 per cent and utilization of steel plates from 95 per cent to 98 per cent; in the Soochow Printing Plant paper utilization increased from 94·8 per cent to 98·62 per cent, by rational cutting.

In Tsinan Diesel Engine Plant, three work sections raised the efficiency of machine tools by 25 per cent. In the Peking No. 1 Cotton Mill, the number of persons tending each doffing machine was reduced from four to three. In the Tsingtoo State Owned Cotton Mill No. 1, a person attending 48 looms could increase this number by 4 or 5, while shortening his route of 60–70 *li* (a *li* is a little bit more than half a kilometer) by 7 *li*. Other applications were said to have been made in coal mines, and in ceramic, brewing, and garments industries. For the last one, a uniform measure system was proposed. A proposal to shape cans in an optimal way, using minimum material for a maximum capacity, which can be extended to all containers and furnace bodies, bellows for a forge, chimneys, gave the possibility to say that capitalists deliberately give the public merely the *illusion* of substantiality.(35)

Agriculture

Here L.P. has been applied to distribution and composition of labour power, location of threshing grounds and granaries, crop layout, irrigation ditches planning, manure transportation, mess-hall running, rational mating of livestock, etc. In this connection even the word "commune-mathematics" has appeared.(36) The Ch'enchuang Commune in Ch'ufu country increases its wheat harvesting speed by about 100 per cent by rational arrangement of threshing grounds and rational organization of labour power. The No. 10 team of the Tachin Brigade in West Suburb Commune of Tich'eng county, having made by L.P. a scheme for a multiple-crop area, taking into consideration different soils, different harvesting periods and crop strains with different adaptability, could step up vegetable output by 14·4 per cent. The No. 7 team of the Nanch'u Brigade in Tich'eng Commune, Ninqyang county, changed single trips into return trips of manure and crop transportation thus raising labour efficiency by 46 per cent. Adjusting through L.P. the composition of labour power for picking cotton brought the Hsiang Chuang team of Chaohung Commune in Liuch'ing town a 100 per cent increase of its efficiency. Average picking per person was raised from 80 to 159 catties a day.(37) In Weihsing Commune, Paksien, rational application of fertilizer stepped up the value of production by 26·7 per cent. In addition, using the simplex method, they worked out a rational layout of crops, saving 55 labor units, 100 catties of fertilizer, with the prospect of raising income by more than 62,000 yuan(38) (equivalent to about $26,300 at official 1959 rates). In 1960 the 1 July People's Commune near Shanghai applied O.R. and saved 40 per cent of their manpower for autumn harvesting, a total of some 210,000 man-days.(39) T'angshan Normal College helped a production brigade's mess-hall in applying O.R., thereby reducing the number of cooks from eleven to eight and the time for commune members to buy their meals from 20 to 5 minutes.(39a)

An assignment scheme for Yuchli Commune in Changsha city, proposed by mathematical workers of the Hunan Institute of Computing Techniques, raised labor efficiency by 10–30 per cent.(39a)

Post and Telecommunications

Again from Tsinan it has been reported that its Post and Telecommunications Bureau applied L.P., thus succeeding in delivering six central newspapers to their subscribers 13 hours earlier and mail 1–1½ hours earlier, while postmen could shorten their working hours by about 2 hours. This was achieved by changing the delivery shifts from three to four without adding postmen, by changing combined delivery of letters and newspapers into separate delivery and by changing the routes of delivery. In Lanchow (Kansu Province) national papers were delivered 14 hours earlier to readers, after L.P. had been applied, while combining thirty delivery sections in Ch'enkwanchu into twenty-five, thereby doing without five postmen and five bicycles, which cut down expenses 3,500 yuan a year.(40)

Water conservancy

Only one concrete example has been given and even that is not an example of operating reservoirs: at the Lo-k'ou and Wang Wang-Chang work-sites, application of L.P. resulted in shortening the line of earth transportation, thereby saving 380,000 working days. In this field Hua Lo-keng advocates to proceed as follows: by summing up and raising indigenous methods of operating small mass-built reservoirs, it will be easy to operate the medium reservoirs undertaking irrigation and power-generation, while experience with the last ones makes it easy to operate the big reservoirs, undertaking irrigation, power-generation and navigation. This would give quick economic results and practical methods.

Further Applications

Hua Lo-keng mentions that O.R. is applicable "to national defense in many ways",(41) but doesn't agree that O.R. is so useful as "to decide, through preparing operation plans in a tent, the victory of a battle waged a thousand *li* away" as an old Chinese saying states.(42) The "weapons are everything" theory is absurd, and over-exaggeration of O.R. is also incorrect. One introductory article on the Theory of Queue Forming by Yueh Min-Yi(43) mentions as fields of application:

(a) storage, in reservoirs, of merchandise, of grain, in registration of out-patients in hospitals;
(b) communications: train schedules, highway traffic, aircraft navigation and landing, using and designing of vessels and wharves;
(c) machinery maintenance;
(d) classifying telephones;
(e) number registering machines, etc.

but this article gives no examples of applications already made in practice. Elsewhere examples are very scarcely reported, some of which we have mentioned already. It seems that although the applicability of queueing theory is recognized, manpower is not yet available for these applications. Some other reported applications of L.P. are e.g. the layout of commercial network, establishment of grain and cotton procurement centers, layout of building sites, passenger service, harbour handling capacities, cities with narrow streets, fisheries. One article of 1 November 1960(44) mentions "we have begun to grope for typical experience in applying L.P. to national economic plans", to which we come back later on.

Summing up the reports on application of O.R. we see clear applications in transportation, apparently at first in long-distance transportation, later on also in short-distance transportation, with its typical difficulty of combining several means of transportation such as men, handcarts, junks, etc., and in the co-ordination of these means. Gradually the necessity of studying the greater system of transport and supply has been recognized. Also, outside transportation nearly all applications are those of L.P., assignment and allocation problems, rational material cutting, etc. Remarkably little mention is made of inventory problems as such. After all, a clear view to which degree O.R. has been applied is not to be got by the reports, due especially to the want of information after March 1961. The emphasis in February 1961 on the perseveration of Tsining Municipal Transp. Comp. could suggest a want of perseveration at other places, as does the recommendation to apply O.R. which appeared at the same moment.(45) Did reports from local papers not reach us, or has there been no reports, or was there little to be reported at all? We must bear in mind that the time of application is still very short and that repeatedly reports appear in China not in order to bring news but mainly in order to support national or local actions, which in our case were already launched in 1960.

Generally one gets the impression that many "applications" which appeared during the movement were more or less common-sense efficiency improvements, evoked by the discovery or recognition of their possibility at all. This breaking through a stagnant situation appears an important by-product of the movement.

FRICTIONS IN THE STORY

Nevertheless, we can get some further information by looking at some difficulties that came up with the introduction of L.P. Obvious are the difficulties of the shortage of mathematically trained personnel, and therefore of the necessity to popularize L.P. and to devise simple methods, and the difficulty that O.R. theories had not been well developed.

Besides, we find in the reports the following indications. On one hand, difficulties came from the side of mathematicians. It has been reported that "some held the view that theory was the essence of mathematics, L.P. was not the main task of mathematics", or "that they want to gain personal credit, which tables and graphs don't give" instead of "to serve production"(46) or that they thought "the masses could not learn L.P." Another objection against some mathematicians was that they "could not enough go into the thick of reality, building ties with the masses" or, having done so, could not "grasp theory and achieve deviation actively".(47) Here one must bear in mind that repeatedly in China intellectuals must endure reproaches for individualism, unpracticability, etc. It has been reported that "when teachers and students in the field could

not find out problems or more problems"—to which to apply L.P.
—"they repeatedly studied *On Practice* by Mao Tse-tung".(48)
This pamphlet of 1937 is a kind of Marxist espistemology, repudi-
ating doctrinairism and empiricism as subjectivist mistakes, describing the process of knowledge in three stages, in a necessary order;
at first real practical perception, that must lead to, secondly, con-
ception, judgment, and inference, that must be based on experience,
but in turn must be concluded by, thirdly, returning to practice,
being applied to reality as a test and condition for further development. No comment is necessary.(48a)

Furthermore it is honestly recognized that some managers
and workers did not promote L.P., fearing troubles, their inability
to learn it and devaluation of their practical experience.(49) Also
the neglect of difficult instructions in favour of easy ones is re-
proached.(50) Sometimes the question seems to have been raised by
workers and peasants, what at all there was new in L.P., because
formerly so many optima had been found by experience. This
question has been carefully handled.(50a) There is the obvious
answer that more complex or big systems, such as integrated
transport and supply systems and the numerous new organizational
systems which arise in a newly developing country, for which
systems there is no adequate experience, are not easily surveyed. But
on the other hand repeatedly the close linking-up of L.P. to the
indigenous "wisdom of the masses" is stressed, understandably in
China. Hua Lo-keng mentions that the "Graphical Method" was
devised by transport workers and that not until 1958 during the big
leap forward was a rigorous proof of it given by mathematicians.(50b)

SIDELIGHTS

It may be of interest to give some short information on fields more
or less related to O.R. in China. In 1958, a Russian analogue
computer arrived; in 1959, a large high-speed computer was
made with the aid of Russian technicians, and also a digital computer

to be used in relation to the output of a power station, while in October 1959 a high-speed computer for general purpose got ready, with 4200 tubes, 4000 diodes, 4000 capacities, 100,000 magnetic cores, 2 memory drums with a total capacity of 6000 bits, an add–subtract speed of 65–153 microseconds, 180 kilowatt power, while Peking radio reported that it was used to determine the water-flow at San Men Gorge, the place where one of the first big dams has been built in the Yellow River.

Since 1956 individual Chinese scientists have turned their attention to the problem of machine translation. After Chinese specialists had become acquainted with Russian results in this field, experiments started in China in 1958 at the Institute of Computer Techniques of the Academy of Sciences in co-operation with the Institute of Linguistics of the Academy of Sciences, and other institutes, with the aid of Soviet specialists. In 1959 it was reported that the main interest was centered on compiling Russian–Chinese and English–Chinese algorithms, with preliminary studies on translation from French and German. The first version of a Russian–Chinese algorithm, based on morphological and structural analysis, had been compiled and was being improved and prepared for programming.

There is no indication that already a kind of O.R. society in China has been formed, as is the case with automation. A communication reports that the Automation Society held in December 1961 in Tientsin its Annual Convention, where forty-eight scientific papers were read on optimum control, stochastic inference, non-linear theory and the input-system, and discussion was on theories of automation and automatic control, automatic elements, computing techniques and automation of production. In 1956 the Chinese Academy of Sciences founded its Institute of Automation and Remote Control at Peking. In November 1958 I came across two examples of the interest in automation in a student exhibition of the results of the combination of education with productive labour in Peking, viz. a working model on a 1 : 5 scale of an automatic tram, stopping e.g. automatically for crossing traffic, and an automatic tractor to be tended at some distance radiographically.

Although, as mentioned, we find after March 1961 very little explicit information on applications or possible applications of O.R. (L.P.), we find some indications of the present "economic climate", as a background against which such applications can be made. Indeed, we can. But we would exceed the scope of this paper if we made more than some short remarks which in no way try to delineate the present economic stituation in China in general. Since 1961, after 3 years of the Big Leap Forward, a general policy of readjustment based on the experiences during the B.L. has been followed, with emphasis on agriculture, the interdependence and proportionate development of different sectors of national economy, the quality and variety of products and the lowering of production costs. Firstly, a lively interest is being shown for all problems concerning the economic accounting system, to be strengthened at present, as is testified by several articles in the main papers and journals, as *People's Daily*, *Kung-Jen Jih-Pao* and even *Red Flag*, the theoretical journal of the CCP,(51) which states: "the task of socialist economic accounting is to compute the economic result of labour through which to reduce the expenditure of labour (living labour) and material (materialized labour)". This concerns mainly enterprises, as a basis. "Each enterprise must set up independently a financial unit", but "specialized accounting must be linked with popular economic accounting at the shift and brigade level",(52) "team and section business accounting".(53)

But "the masses" are urged to take part not only in the collection of data but also in the analysis of economic activity directed to the lowering of production costs, according to one article in the Ta-kung Pao(54) of October 1961 which describes such an analysis in a commune. Nevertheless, the examples given in the article don't give the impression that any very difficult mathematical methods were used. At the same time in contrast with the emphasis on mass-activity, we have to mention that in enterprises the "responsibility system" is being emphasized, in which tasks and responsibilities of employees are defined clearly, apparently in reaction to the former years during which sometimes everybody was doing everything.

P

In general all leading personnel are urged to give much attention to enterprise management and control and analysis of economic activity,(55) not only at the level of the plant, but also of the workshop, with attention e.g. to cost of production, labor productivity, quality of products and overhaul and inspection of machinery, which apparently had been neglected. Nevertheless, no mention is made of the use of refined mathematical methods.

In addition to this it has been discovered that "the material supplies stored in the warehouses, enterprises, food departments, railway stations, state farms, etc., throughout the country exceed the normal stock requirements or are not needed according to this year's plans". (56) This surplus is apparently mainly caused by hoarding, made in order to fulfil production tasks in case of shortage of supply, and, maybe, through insufficient insight in the losses induced by too much storing. One tries to centralize inventory "placing the interests of the State above all". This whole problem is a good field for O.R. applications but no explicit mention of them has been made.

Besides these practical developments a lively interest has been shown since 1961 in the theory of economics and economic development. On the last subject, in December 1961, a long article appeared in the *People's Daily*(57) and a discussion-meeting of workers in economics and economic theory was held in Peking on how to develop the study of these subjects. The main topics were the appropriate proportions between agriculture, light industry and heavy industry, the appropriate proportion of accumulation and consumption and the factors which determined speed and proportion.(58)

During discussion, emphasis was repeatedly laid upon the quantitative aspect of these problems and the necessity to collect data and to use exact methods of economics and mathematics for comprehensive planning, an effort in which only a beginning had been made. The same quantitative interest was to be found at a similar meeting discussing further research on economic effect (e.e.). Here some topics were e.g. the standard for e.e., the relation between immediate e.e. and remote e.e., between individual and social e.e., difficulties in computing e.e., the comparative e.e. of investment projects. Penetrating investigation on such questions was strongly advocated.(59) In this context an important article appeared in the *People's Daily* of 1 August 1961 on "The Economic–Mathematical Method" to which we come return in the following section.

THE EVALUATION BY THE RÉGIME

If we want to evaluate the application of O.R. in China, as reported, it can be interesting to show some points of evaluation by the Chinese régime itself. We can get an impression of them if we read several articles in the main journals which give this evaluation.

L.P. has been defined as "a branch of knowledge which calls for the use of mathematical and economic methods to study the way of employing the least manpower as well as material and financial resources to fulfil a task to the maximum effect".(60) Thus it is in complete agreement with the "general line" for economic activity, dating from the spring of 1958, "to get greater, quicker, better and more economical results", because it tackles at the same time the problem of maximizing production with fixed means (greater, quicker) and of minimizing means when production is fixed (more economical), and thus it can go on now that after the Big Leap Forward emphasis has been laid upon more economical results. In addition Hua Lo-keng mentions its useful characteristic, that for physically quite different situations the same model can be used, on the condition of eventual flexible adjustment according to circumstances. He also remarks that L.P. "is fit for the small and is more so for the big", but in the last case "it is necessary to use computing instruments".(61)

As to the usefulness, it is stated in several places that many organizational systems are so complicated, or seemingly simple systems are so interconnected with others, that using mathematics to calculate the optimum is necessary and that nobody can be blamed for having not reached such an optimum before using L.P.(62) In that case "L.P. is the simplest and the most straightforward method which can be used quickly and has an easy graphical representation".

Understandably the first reports are very enthusiastic, with striking examples showing the great power of L.P., but later reports are more moderate and cautious, stating that L.P. "can be developed" for a wide variety of uses,(63) "played a useful part",(64) has been of definite use in the sphere of production and construction as a branch of beforehand planning"(65) and Hua Lo-keng even states explicitly "while L.P. can play a great part, we must correctly recognize its limitations", "it itself can neither discover some unknown factors, nor take account of man's subjective activity" and "we should on no account over-stress 'method' and overlook 'subjective' efforts".(66) Nevertheless we can say that generally on the practical level L.P. has got a definitely favorable reception.

Now turning to the ideological level, the whole "L.P. movement" as a part of the drive to combine education—to which later on sometimes research has been added—with productive labor is praised for several positive effects: beside having helped production it has broken through the "superstition" that mathematics is not applicable and only a case of experts. Further, the mathematicians are said to have gained more "political consciousness, estimation for the masses of workers and peasants, concrete feelings and perceptual knowledge," etc.(67) At last in several places it has been emphasized that mathematical research has been stimulated and teaching methods improved.

More than once also in applying L.P. the necessity of political command and subordination to party policy is stressed. But now, in view of the only very recent interest in East European countries for extensively and practically using mathematics in economic research and planning,(68) what about the ideological evaluation of mathematical applications in economic matters in China? The article of Wu Chia-p'ei in the *People's Daily* of 1 August 1961 throws light on the subject.(69) The humble introduction, "Although I am merely a beginner", similar to an article of Hua Lo-keng on O.R., seems to give away the writer as an expert. The fact that Marx, Lenin and

Mao Tse-tung can be and indeed are cited in favour of using mathematics seems to show how fundamentally mathematics has been accepted already.(70) As main topics of the "economic–mathematical method" we can mention: analysis of formation of price, reproduction, balance of connections and potentialities of the products between different enterprises, the calculation of population and labour resources, together with analysis of changes of market demands, models of the economic process, analysis of production relationship between departments, optimal planning, etc.

Four reasons are mentioned for the rise of the "economic–mathematical method" under the socialist system, which in the beginning of the article it is admitted that communist countries began to use in the late fifties of this century: (1) "The development of economic science calls for a deeper analytical study of quantity relationships simultaneously with a continual penetrating study of quality so that we may more effectively appreciate and make use of economic laws." (2) "With the tremendous upsurge of the national economy, planning requirements become even greater and the importance of long-term planning daily becomes more apparent . . ." and the usual methods are too slow and inaccurate. (3) Technical innovations raise the social productivity rate on the basis of mechanization and automation, new technical conditions and improved production administration and labor organization and better economic evaluation of the innovations. (4) The large scale of the national economy makes using high-speed computers necessary. In itself mathematics are considered to be neutral. "Mathematical methods are only a means". Once divorced from Marxist economic theory and formally ill-used, they become merely "mathematical games". Also, in the Chinese and Russian publications much effort is done to show that their methods are quite different from the Western, although the mathematical content may be the same. Besides it is stated that only in socialist countries "real O.R. and mathematical economics" can be used, because only there "can all the national interests of the people be taken into account". On one occasion(71) the remarkable question is raised whether L.P. is not a wrong method, when for example it advocates "to plant less and yield more", for maximizing profit, while as much planting as possible is necessary. It seems to us that in that case the mathematical model is wrongly stated, especially as to the objective function. More serious seems the question whether or not "constant" conditions change sometimes rapidly.(72)

Klein, Tinbergen and Leontieff are mentioned as the outstanding specialists but mainly "they are using their methods for bad purposes". In contrast to the theoretical works on general political economic problems "the study of the Western works describing the practical value of economic studies" is advocated "to understand some phenomena of the capitalist economy and use some methods of economic analysis".

Returning to our point we can conclude that the importance of mathematical methods in macro- and micro-economics is well understood in China, and that, although Western use of the methods is criticized, no ideological barrier seems to hinder the further introduction of them in China.

CONCLUSION

The question whether in China O.R. has been used much or little loses sense in view of the need for a measure. Of course the development of O.R. and its applications are in no way comparable to those in many industrial countries, but that is certainly not a good measure. For accurate comparison with other big Asian countries we have not enough material at hand. Japan and India have both a markedly longer history in applied mathematics. No attempt has been made in this paper to deal with the question to which degree O.R. indeed can be applied at present in China.

Nevertheless, we can make the following concluding remarks. Evidently O.R. has been introduced in China and the idea of L.P. has spread more or less widely. Remarkable features are the popularization of L.P., for which the use of mass movements appears to be a means. After many remarkable examples of successful applications of L.P. there are not enough indications to make a judgment whether and in which degree these applications spread further, while also more technical information on the applications is lacking. Besides practical improvements some of the main results may have been the insight acquired by showing that efficiency improvements are indeed possible. It seems likely that O.R. techniques other than L.P. have been used only relatively scarcely and incidentally. Inside the educational and research institutes active tackling of O.R. problems and their foundations has begun. One gets the impression that, although the transport sector especially is still likely to reap the benefit of L.P., more attention is given to a strengthening of management and data collection, which is quite understandable. Besides, a further training of mathematicians is necessary. Nevertheless, especially in these years of readjustment, China appears to have become rapidly and well aware of the importance of mathematical methods in all sorts of economic activities.

NOTES

(1) We give here a not exhaustive list of these translated articles, with an indication where their translation is to be found. We will refer to them further on in the notes simply by indicating their corresponding letter, and the indication of pages refers to the translations.

Abbreviations

C.B. = Current Background, Hongkong
J.M.J.P. = Jen-min Jih-pao (People's Daily), Peking
K.M.J.P. = Kuang-ming Jih-pao, Peking
N.C.N.A. = New China News Agency, Peking
S.C.M.M. = Selections from China Mainland Magazines, Hongkong
S.C.M.P. = Survey of China Mainland Press, Hongkong

a. "Shantung makes Extensive Use of 'Yun Ch'ou Hsueh' (Science of Operation and Programming = Operations Research) to Unearth Production Potential." J.M.J.P. 29 July 1960 (S.C.M.P. 2324, 24 August 1960, 15–18).
b. "The Revelation of Mathematics" by Chiang Hui. J.M.J.P. 29 July 1960 (S.C.M.P. 2324, 24 August 1960, 19–20).
c. "What is the Science of Operation and Programming?" J.M.J.P.

29 July 1960 (S.C.M.P. 2324, 24 August 1960, 20–21).

d. "Practical Application and Theoretical Discussion of Operations Research at Ch'u-Fou Normal College, Shantung." J.M.J.P. 29 July 1960 (Partly transl. in Operations Research 9, 3, May–June 1961, 419–421).

e. "Kansu Tries Out Linear Programming with Success." K.M.J.P. 11 October 1960 (C.B. 649, 5 April 1960, 35–36).

f. "Mathematics and Mechanics Faculty at Hopei University Applies 'Yun Ch'ou Hsueh' in Service of Production." K.M.J.P. 27 October 1960 (C.B. 649, 5 April 1961, 32–34).

g. " 'Yun Ch'ou Hsueh', a New Branch of Science Applied in National Economic Construction" by Hua Lo-keng. K.M.J.P. 1 November 1960 (C.B. 649, 5 April 1961, 1–13).

h. "Mass Movement Spreads in Shantung for Linear Programming of 'Yun Ch'ou Hsueh' " by Ting Tsung-Yueh. K.M.J.P. 1 November 1960 (C.B. 649, 5 April 1961, 22–27).

i. "The Mass Movement for Promoting Development of Production, Advancing Pedagogy and Scientific Research, and Introducing 'Yun Ch'ou Hsueh' in a Big Way" by Chao Tzu-sheng. K.M.J.P. 1 November 1960 (C.B. 649, 5 April 1960, 28–31).

j. "Make use of 'Yun Ch'ou Hsueh' for Serving Socialist Construction" by Liu Chi-p'ing. Hung-Ch'i (Red Flag), 1960, No. 20–21, 1 November 1960, 44 ff. (S.C.M.M., No. 236, 21 November 1960). My grateful acknowledgement to the Sinological Institute at Leyden, which was so kind as to translate this article, as the S.C.M.M. translation was not accessible.

k. "What I have Learned from Popularization of Linear Programming in the Countryside" by Ch'i Min-yu. K.M.J.P. 17 December 1960 (C.B. 649, 5 April 1961, 37–42).

l. "Faculty Members and Students of Department of Mathematics, Wuhan University, Popularize Science of Planning and Programming for Promoting Agricultural Production." K.M.J.P. 17 December 1960 (C.B. 649, 5 April 1961, 43–45).

m. "What is Theory of Queue Forming?" by Yueh Min-yi. J.M.J.P. 3 February 1961 (C.B. 649, 5 April 1961, 14–17).

n. "Some Economic Applications of the Science of Planning and Programming" by Yun Ch'uan. J.M.J.P. 12 March 1961 (C.B. 649, 5 April 1961, 18–21).

o. "Yun Ch'ou Hsueh Extensively Applied in Production." N.C.N.A. 13 March 1961 (C.B. 649, 5 April 1961, 46–47).

p. "Operations Research Blossoms in China" by Hua Lo-keng. China Reconstructs, X.8, August 1961, 24–27.

q. "Tsining Municipal Transportation Company Perseveres in Carrying Out Linear Programming in Short-Distance Transportation." Ta-kung Pao, 27 February 1962 (S.C.M.P. 2699, 16 March 1962, 18–19).

r. "Make Use of Linear Programming to Serve Short Distance

Transportation" by Hsin Chia-chou. Ta-kung Pao, 27 February 1962 (S.C.M.P. 2699, 16 March 1962, 18–19).

(2) George N. Ecklund: "Communist China tries Linear Programming." Asian Survey, Berkeley, I.7, September 1961, 27–31.

(3) Liao Lu-Yen: *The Whole Party and the Whole People Go In for Agriculture in a Big Way* (Peking, Foreign Languages Press, 1960).

(4) l 45, j.

(5) h 22.

(6) j.

(7) i 29.

(8) h 22.

(9) g, p and Kexue Tongbao (Scientia), 26 October 1959, 18 (1959), 562–567 (tr. in the A.M.S. Notices 6, 7, part I, December 1959).

(10) Only p q 5.

(11) E.g. j, p.

(12) g 2 ff., p.

(12a) Some remarks might be useful. These methods apply of course only to flows of the same goods or of empty cars as is indicated only in r 20. The drawings taken from Chinese articles are very simplified, viz. only one closed circuit, one direction and no amounts of the transported goods are indicated, but nevertheless the central idea is clear, and one oneself can make more involved examples. Evidently e.g. the change of direction after detection of detour deals only with the smallest amount in the original scheme with detour.

(13) p 27.

(14) g 4.

(15) p 27. In this article the problem is formulated in a slightly different, less correct way.

(16) h 26, j.

(17) m.

(18) E.g. b 19, d 421, i 30, j, and Kexue Tongbao 18 (1959), 562–567 see note 23.

(19) See (18) and K.M.J.P. 22 January 1962 (S.C.M.P. 2676, 12 February 1962).

(20) K.M.J.P. 22 January 1962 (S.C.M.P. 2676, 12 February 1962).

(21) a 17.

(22) See (20) and N.C.N.A. Hofei, 6 March 1962 (S.C.M.P. 2704, 23 March 1962, p. 18).

(23) Hua Lo-keng: "Mathematical Research in China in the Last Ten Years." Kexue Tongbao (*Scientia*), 18 (1959), 565–567 (Chinese) (tr. in the A.M.S. Notices 6, 7, part I, December 1959 and partly in Bulletin of the O.R.S.A., Operations Research 8, suppl. 1, 1960, B51–B55) and Marshall H. Stone: "Mathematics in Continental China, 1949–1960." A.M.S. Notices, 8, 3, No. 54, June 1961.

(24) Chinese Mathematics—Acta, A.M.S., Providence.

(25) Wu Wen-tsun: "A Remark on the Fundamental Theorem in the Theory of Games." Sci. Rec. (N.S.) 3 (1959), 229–233. Wu Wen-sun:

"On Non-co-operative Games with Restricted Domains of Activities."
Sci. Sin, August (1961), X, 4, x 387–410.

(26) Yuh, M. J.: "On the Problem M/M/n in the Theory of Queues." Acta
Math. Sin. 9 (1959), 494–502 (Chin., Engl. summ.) = Sci. Rec. (M.S.)
3 (1959), 614–615 (two theorems are demonstrated for $P_k(t)$, the probability of the presence of k customers at time t). Wang, Tzu-kwen: "On a
Birth and Death Process." Sci-Rec. (M.S.) 3 (1959), 331–334.

(27) Wu, Chang-pu: "The Optimum Operation for a Yearly Regulated
Water Reservoir." Sci. Rec. vol. 4, No. 2, February (1960), 108–110.
(The procedure of J. D. C. Little (O.R.3 (1955), 187–197) is generalized,
taking flood control in consideration, with the extra condition, that the
probability of flooding above the reservoir is bounded above by a constant less than unity.)

(28) i 30, j, n 18.

(29) E.g. n 26.

(30) r 21–22.

(31) h 23.

(32) a 16, p 25.

(33) f 33.

(34) q 19.

(35) g 8.

(36) d 420, i 30.

(37) h 24.

(38) f 32.

(39) p 24.

(39a) o 46.

(40) e 35.

(41) g 11.

(42) c 19.

(43) m 16–17.

(44) h 25.

(45) q, r.

(46) j, k.

(47) h 27.

(48) d 420, i 29.

(48a) Mao Tse Tung: *On Practice* (Foreign Languages Press, Peking 1951),
23 pages.

(49) o 47.

(50) r 21.

(50a) E.g. h 18, k 41, p 24.

(50b) g 4 and Kexue Tongbao, 18 (1959) (see note 23).

(51) E.g. J.M.J.P. 14 November (1961) (S.C.M.P. 2660, 17 January (1962)),
Ta-kung Pao, 25 December (1961) (S.C.M.P. 2660, 17 January (1962)),
Hung-ch'i, No. 23, 1 December (1961) (S.C.M.M. 292, 18 January
(1961)).

(52) J.M.J.P. 24 December (1961) (S.C.M.P. 2660, 17 January (1962)).

(53) Kung-jen Jih-Pao, 5, 6, 7, 8, 9 and 10 September (1961) (C.B. 673, 4 December (1961)).
(54) Ta-kung Pao, 25 October (1961) (S.C.M.P. 2624, 22 November (1961)).
(55) Ta-kung Pao, 2 February (1962) (S.C.M.P. 2687, 28 February (1962)).
(56) J.M.J.P. 15 March (1962) (S.C.M.P. 2707, 28 March (1962)).
(57) J.M.J.P. 27 December (1961) (S.C.M.P. 2670, 31 January (1962)).
(58) K.M.J.P. 15 November (1961) (S.C.M.P. 2640, 15 December (1961)).
(59) J.M.J.P. 20 January (1962) (S.C.M.P. 2675, 9 February (1962)).
(60) c 19.
(61) g 13.
(62) g 2, r 20.
(63) j.
(64) f 33.
(65) J.M.J.P. 1 August (1961) (S.C.M.P. 2582, 20 September (1961)) p. 1, 6.
(66) g 13.
(67) j.
(68) See e.g. United Nations Economic Bulletin for Europe, vol. 12, No. 1, Geneva (1960), and a series of Russian articles, transl. in Problems of Economics, New York, III, No. 7, November (1960).
(69) Wu Chia-p'ei: "On 'The Economic–Mathematical Method.' " J.M.J.P. 1 August (1961) (S.C.M.P. 2582, 20 September (1901), 1–8).
(70) Marx: "a science might only be said to have attained true perfection when it has successfully used mathematics" (*Reminiscences of Marx and Engels*, p. 73). Lenin: "Lenin always emphasized the fact that economy should make a careful study of mathematics and references in order that the maximum possible use be made of theoretical conclusions in actual practice." Mao Tse-tung: "Comrade Mao Tse-tung advises us to pay strict attention to the quantity aspect of facts and problems, and here fundamental quantity analysis should be used."
(71) k 38.
(72) In this case repeated application of L.P. or the methods proceeding from the final simplex tableau of the former, slightly different case can be used, but may be they require yet just a little bit too much insight from persons which apply L.P. mechanically.

12

CAPITAL/LABOR RATIOS AND THE INDUSTRIALIZATION OF WEST AFRICA

EDWARD MARCUS

Professor of Economics, Brooklyn College, Brooklyn 10, New York, U.S.A.

AND

MILDRED RENDL MARCUS

Lecturer in Economics, Columbia University, 2 Peter Cooper Road, New York 10, N.Y., U.S.A.

As PART of its development armory West Africa is striving to establish manufacturing industries, thereby lessening its dependence on imports and eventually increasing local living standards. A concomitant problem is the degree of capitalization (the capital/labor ratio) that should be employed to attain the desired goal. This is a problem for operations research; it is the determination of the optimum production function for a developing economy.

The constraints within which West Africa must work are: (i) the available supplies of capital, both from foreign aid and private domestic and foreign sources, that would be available to the manufacturing sector provided the profit possibilities are sufficiently attractive; (ii) the extent of the domestic market for the output of each specific installation, that is, the plant capacity and attendant production function that would be most economical; (iii) the available supply of labor that can be drawn from the rural sector;

and (iv) the productivity of labor—in turn a function of training (with its implications for start-up costs). The productivity of labor, of course, will in part be influenced by the degree of mechanization (the capital/labor ratio). The most controversial factor is the capital/labor ratio. The conflicting views can be summarized briefly.

Those favoring a low ratio draw their main arguments from orthodox economic theory. Labor is abundant and cheap in West Africa, as in all underdeveloped areas, while capital is scarce and expensive. Wherever possible, therefore, labor should be substituted, if this will reduce per unit costs, that is, if production is maintained and the saving on capital costs more than offsets the added wages bill. In addition, by releasing capital, e.g. from the materials transfer step (lowering the capital/labor ratio) a given amount of investment results in more jobs, or alternatively, a given output can be obtained with a smaller quantity of capital.

Critics of this view stress the connection between the capital/labor ratio, productivity, and income per worker. The greater the degree of capitalization, the greater is productivity. Wages, and thus incomes, are correspondingly higher. Furthermore, the more intense the use of machinery, the greater the need for a more skilled labor force. The process implies increased training. A capital/labor ratio comparable to one which exists in highly industrialized countries would aid the competitiveness of the new factory. Since alternative incomes in agriculture are so low, factory wages can be set below those in the Western world and still be high compared with alternative income. The result might be a productivity comparable to the Western world, but, with wage rates considerably lower, per unit costs would be able to compete with costs of imported goods.

LOW CAPITAL/LABOR RATIO

With less capital per worker, a given workforce will have a lower output, and *per capita* production will also be lower. Per unit of capital, however, output would be higher than with greater use of capital; thus the lower productivity of a unit of labor will be accompanied by the greater productivity of a unit of capital. The implication of the latter relationship is a profit margin (measured as a percentage of invested capital) greater than in a capital-intensive operation, though the latter's total (absolute) profits might be more. (This does not imply that profit margins would be greater than in other areas. It would only be greater in this area than in a more capital-intensive operation).

What determines whether the ratio will be high or low? The answer is a combination of technical considerations and comparative costs. The former, of course, is a limitation in the more complicated processes; many of the more advanced techniques cannot be done by hand. In this case the requirements of capital and labor per unit of output are rigid, and thus the ratio of capital to labor is equally inflexible.

On the other hand, many types of work performed by machines can be done by labor and vice versa. Unloading and transporting raw materials can be effected by moving belts, with men guiding trucks or lifts, or by men and women carrying the material in baskets on their heads. This flexibility is especially evident in the smaller plant whose output often is too small to justify the more specialized equipment.[1]

Where this flexibility does exist, the other important consideration is the costs of each factor. If wages are sufficiently low, the same input from many workers can be cheaper than from the more expensive capital component. While other considerations will enter—e.g. a greater use of capital might weaken (or increase) the threat of unionization—a paramount influence will be this relative cost.

The deficiency in this argument lies in its static assumptions. The comparison of the costs and productivities of the factors of production assumes a fixity in the calculations which, in fact, may not exist. The wage rate, for example, is in part a reflection of the laborer's productivity, in turn dependent on his skill. With more machinery

[1] Cf. the *United Nations Industrialization and Productivity Bulletin*, No. 2, March 1959, p. 21.

the worker can be given a know-how he did not have before, thus raising his output. By altering his productivity—a resultant of the capital/labor ratio—we change the relative merits of substituting labor for capital, since increased output per worker means lower labor costs, unless offset by correspondingly higher wage rates. But this greater attractiveness of labor resulted from a prior increase in the capital/labor ratio.

HIGH CAPITAL/LABOR RATIO

The counterpart to the argument of the preceding section can be spelled out in a hypothetical illustration. Assume a factory in the United States whose production function reflects the costliness of American labor and relative abundance of capital. Per unit costs of production reflect both the wages spread out over the high output per worker and the depreciation and other capital costs of the equipment.

If an identical plant were to be set up in West Africa, and if the workers could be trained to operate the machines as efficiently, the same output per worker would result as in the United States, capital costs would presumably be the same, but wage costs per unit of output would be considerably lower, reflecting the lower wage rates in the area. The greater output of the African in industry would permit a wage much higher than in other local occupations, yet lower than in the United States. As a result, selling prices would be below that of the American product while wages would be higher than in the absence of this plant.

However, if this plant substituted labor for capital, the gains to labor's productivity would diminish, and with it would go the means of raising wage levels and still maintain competitiveness. Each replacement of the machined operation by a worker reduces the need for a skilled employee and thus replaces a more productive and trained worker by a less skilled operator. Both wages and output per worker decline, and thus the impact on per unit costs is lessened.

Of course, the possibility of a highly mechanized factory implies that the greater output would find a market. If such a plant must produce 10,000 units to reach optimum operating rates, while the demand is for only 1000 units, output would have to be cut back, thus raising capital costs per unit and ending the advantageous cost position. On the other hand, if the market is large enough to support one such factory but not two, then, rather than have each working at partial (higher cost) capacity, it might be advisable policy to permit only one—in effect, a monopoly—with restrictions on its price and profits freedom.[2] Alternatively, equipment producers might expand their research efforts to include the designing of equipment that would be equally efficient even though designed for smaller scale operations.[3] If this could be achieved, there would be less pressure on producers to continue to produce a large volume in order to cover part of overhead costs. With the use of machines designed for smaller capacities, the size of plant could be better adjusted to the market, and the pressure of over-capacity on prices removed. Supply would then become more elastic, and over-supply situations more quickly corrected, thus reducing the periods of uneconomic prices and low profits (or even losses), and accompanying solvency dangers.

In determining the appropriate industries to be established, an obvious consideration is the size of the market over the near future. An additional consideration, of particular significance for items whose value is small in relation to bulk, is the proximity to raw materials. It is these two factors which make it inadvisable to attempt to establish basic iron and steel industries in most of the West African countries. Only Nigeria has any sizeable coal deposits—and these are proving to be not too profitable to mine—while iron ore has been found only in the extreme western sector, in Sierra Leone, Guinea, and Liberia. Add to this the poor inter-country transport facilities, and it can be seen why the input side makes such an industry doubtful for the area. An additional reenforcement is the limited market for the finished product. No West African country is a significant pro-

---

[2] In Kenya, for example, a government limitation on the number of firms has been necessary, especially in textiles and building materials.

[3] Cf. *Productivity Bulletin*, No. 2, p. 23.

ducer of metal products that require large quantities of iron or steel. On the other hand, light consumer goods—textiles, processed food, bicycles—would find a market.

Another danger is extremely high capital/labor ratios, particularly in those cases where the large-scale exploitation of natural resources appears feasible. This can be illustrated from the experience of the Gabon and Congo Republics. The Gabon, with less than half a million population, is endowed with tremendous deposits of iron ore, manganese, petroleum, and uranium. As a result, large amounts of European and American capital are flowing in—perhaps upwards of half a billion dollars will be invested during the decade of the 'sixties. For a country whose average daily wage is less than $1 a day, there is obviously a tremendous possibility for raising living standards.

To some extent the funds are going into extending the country's infrastructure, especially the construction of new railroads. But a large part of the funds will be directed towards highly mechanized excavation operations, resulting in capital/labor ratios as high as $100,000 per man or even more. Much of these funds will not expand job opportunities for the local populace, and thus local figures imply. The required skills are far beyond existing abilities, so that expatriates must be brought in on a large scale.[4]

SOME INTERNAL REPERCUSSIONS

It may also be objected that industrialization would worsen the terms of trade for agriculture. While there is some hired agricultural labor, it is doubtful that the additional demand from the urban centers for workers would disturb the rural wage structure; farming in West Africa is still mainly the preserve of the family. If anything, it is the level of income in the agricultural region—still the overwhelming employer—which determines wages in the urban centers. That is, urban wages must be sufficiently above the rural level to

[4] For a more complete discussion, cf. E. Marcus, "Large-scale Investment and Development—the Dilemma of the Gabon Republic", *Economic Development and Cultural Change*, **9**, No. 1, Part 1, October 1960.

Q

attract the necessary labor since agriculture is the major alternative employment opportunity for the bulk of the population. Therefore, a step-up of the present pace of industrialization is unlikely to make the cost position of African agriculture labor deteriorate.

The other possibility is an increase in the cost of goods that the farmer buys. This would occur should the new domestic supplier be high cost—higher than the present imports (inclusive of transportation charges)—and if it were accorded tariff protection to offset this disadvantage. But if the newly organized firm is able to raise productivity, a possibility enhanced by its use of equipment that is more efficient than that now commonly employed in the area, the cost, outlook would be that much more favorable, with the attendant lowering of selling prices. Moreover, if such industry used locally produced raw materials, the added demand could push up the farmer's selling prices and improve his terms of trade. Since there is the double savings in transport costs—the raw materials need not be shipped overseas, but to the newly located nearby producer, while the finished product no longer comes from so long a distance—the savings here could offset higher manufacturing costs. As evidence of this potential: on bulkier commodities ocean freight may account for up to one-third of the final price, thus making the purchasing power of a given volume of raw produce on the farm as little as one-half that in the overseas markets.[5]

Actually, the more capital-intensive the project, the less the potential disturbance to the local labor market. Per dollar of investment fewer workers are needed. Fewer workers also means fewer migrants into the area, and auxiliary outlays such as housing, educational facilities, sanitation programs, etc., may also be less.

The current extensive migration to cities in West Africa naturally presents the potential problem of unemployment. A capital-intensive program minimizes the number of jobs, and leaves the prospect of large-scale unemployment.

Since this newly arrived labor is usually unskilled and lacks the

[5] For some examples, cf. the United Africa Company Limited, *Statistical and Economic Review*, No. 19, March 1957, pp. 9 ff.

most basic industrial attitudes, it would be simplest to employ them on social and urban projects, such as the spraying of stagnant waters, in order to reduce the incidence of malaria; construction projects that require little capital and employ a maximum of unskilled labor, thereby also improving the inadequate infrastructure; and other tasks similar to the experience of the United States with the Civilian Conservation Corps in the 1930s. With a minimum of outlay the government would obtain some return for its money in the form of improved infrastructure while the workers employed would have their first taste of the wage-earning economy including initiation in work habits and routines.

The productivity of capital could also be improved by emphasizing government health expenditures. As disease and sickness are reduced, one of the major causes of absenteeism is lessened. Output will be higher, as the effectiveness of the labor force is increased in this way. Then, the capital/output ratio is less, or, in terms of costs, capital charges per unit of production are that much lower. This, in turn, would increase the competitiveness and profits performance.

The preceding analysis suggests that consideration be given to the arguments both for and against a high capital/labor ratio. Thus the most extreme form of the high ratio argument would be a fully automated plant; there would be no local employment and no addition to wages and purchasing power. There would also be no advantage in establishing such a plant in West Africa. The argument rested, in part, on the use of lower wage labor with superior rates of productivity. As a firm's labor component is reduced, the advantage of migration to Africa is reduced. On the other hand, as the capital component is reduced, the worker's output and *per capita* productivity are reduced, as well as his ability to develop new skills. Here again we have failed to achieve our objective. The decision, as will be shown in the discussion of training, rests on the opportunity the installation affords to the African to acquire skill, and proficiency in its application, within a reasonable time. Thus, to install a fully automated plant directed by a bank of computers is unwise, for the possibility of training the African to become a competent computer programmer is a long and doubtful procedure. However, the establishment of a textile plant may be very wise since the various productive operations can be learned within the normal "start-up" period.

THE ROLE OF REPAIR AND MAINTENANCE

Associated with the problem of appropriate capital/labor ratios is repair and maintenance which require high labor components, especially if the repairs reduce the need for replacement parts. In effect, the life of the machine is extended, thus reducing the need for more capital—annual depreciation is less while servicing costs rise. Note that the substitution of labor for capital (the lowering of the capital/labor ratio) and the use of repairs to lengthen the life of equipment both lower the ratio of capital to output, but the latter does so without reducing productivity per productive worker, thus permitting much higher wage rates. Incidentally, repairs and maintenance service centers also serve as training schools, since here, too, more skills are required.

Part of the need for a large amount of training arises from the poor standards which exist. Local raw materials are often so undependable that the progress of processing industries is seriously retarded; this, for example, has been true in Nigeria in regard to rubber.[6] It is, however, possible that even a relatively simple quality-control approach could raise the standards appreciably; this, coupled with the expanded training of labor in servicing, could serve both to raise output and incomes.[7]

An additional economy would arise from the more intensive use of existing equipment. Rates of operation tend to be somewhat lower in underdeveloped than in developed areas, thus making the cost of spare parts a greater proportion of output, since this cost, mainly

[6] Cf. the U.S. Department of Commerce, *Investment in Nigeria* (by B. Blankenheimer) (Washington 1957), p. 39.

[7] Cf. W. R. Pabst, "Use of Statistical Quality Control in the Industry of Under-developed Countries", *Productivity Bulletin*, No. 3, March 1960.

inventory, does not change proportionately to use of productive capacity. To the extent that the part can be fabricated locally, and thus not stocked, capital is released and the cost component is incurred only as needed rather than continuing regardless of scale of operation.

Another aspect of the savings objective is the decrease in loss of operating time due to breakdowns. The more intensive the capital/labor ratio, the more serious is the cost of idle equipment. Therefore, the greater the reliance on local maintenance and repairs, the fewer the interruptions of this nature.

However, it must be realized that the necessary repair operations should not be beyond the capacity of the prospective maintenance men. Otherwise there arises a built-in need for expensive expatriate mechanics or engineers. Whether they are on the spot or, if only infrequently called on, flown in from abroad, costs increase. There obviously is a need for repair simplification—analogous to work simplification[8]—so that the desired steps can be made learnable. Again we have an opportunity for a gradation of skills, the more complicated tasks being reserved for the more experienced, with wages rising correspondingly. It is also wise to install sturdy equipment, for delicate parts are often too difficult for the mechanic with limited skills to handle.[9]

The aim in the maintenance sector is to substitute labor for capital; the existing capital is made to last longer, thus lowering annual capital costs, while the repair and maintenance costs are raised. Since the latter have a high labor component, the training skills of the local labor force are increased and, in addition, savings can be made on foreign exchange because local fabrication reduces the need for overseas replacement parts.

The above statements are not contradicting our thesis—the need to raise capital/labor ratios. The aim is a high ratio of capital to

[8] In the Northern Rhodesian Copperbelt, as a means of upgrading African labor, jobs formerly held by Europeans are broken into several simpler tasks which, together, are equivalent to the original job.

[9] Cf. the characteristics of the Russian "Krasni Proletari" tools (*The Economist*, **199**, No. 6141, 6 May 1961, p. 581).

operating labor. A three-shift staff, for example, would, therefore, be desirable for it permits the most intensive use of available capital. By tripling the number of workers the over-all capital/labor ratio is lowered, but each shift still has a higher ratio. In effect, the capital is made to work three times. As a result, productivity per worker is higher than with a lower ratio and fewer shifts. Since output is a main determinant of income, the use of labor for servicing and the introduction of three shifts both keep individual worker output high, thus permitting higher wages than does the alternative lower ratio. (It is also assumed that depreciation would not rise appreciably with the more intensive rate of operation.)

Training

A basic problem is training, and the rapidity with which it can transform productivity standards to the point where they are comparable with those current in the more industrialized countries. The proposal, therefore, is a capital outlay in the form of technical education, and analogous to proposed tangible investment, the return can be measured by the additional productivity of the trainee. Ideally the discounted value of this additional output—after subtracting auxiliary costs, such as materials, power, etc.—should be more than the educational outlay, and, in fact, so much more that this excess permits both higher wages and a still greater accumulation of capital.

In this instance the government has a definite role to play. While the private concern can certainly institute its own training program—and many African-based companies have excellent ones, such as those run by Unilever's giant United Africa Company—the danger of pirating remains an inhibiting factor. There is too much temptation to allow some other company to bear the training cost—which can often involve hundreds of dollars per trainee per year[10]—and then entice the apprentice away with an offer of a wage somewhat above that promised by the firm undertaking the training. Therefore, at little extra cost, the pirating firm is spared making

[10] Cf. the *Statistical and Economic Review*, No. 22, January 1959, p. 43.

training outlays, as well as the uncertainty involved in the success of its efforts.

If, however, the government undertakes the effort, it need not hold back or restrict the scope of its operations, and it can assure new manufacturers of a reservoir of skilled labor. In return, a suitable tax (e.g. per trainee hired) would assure that only those firms that could really profit from these trained workers would utilize them. The tax would not only help finance the educational program, but also lessen the temptation to hoard skills that are in short supply by putting the trained workers on jobs that require lesser trained personnel. For those companies that prefer to continue their own training programs, and thus bear the educational costs themselves, it might be advisable to allow a tax credit; in effect, this offset would be an approximate compensation for trainees lost to other firms.

To avoid overproduction and thus waste of funds, the available openings for trainees in the government school would be determined on the basis of the industries the nation desired to attract. If woodworking companies were envisioned as economically feasible, while metal-working plants were not, then more carpenters would be trained but fewer machinists. As a result, the would-be furniture company, for example, would find some reservoir of skills to draw on, thus reducing its start-up costs, whereas since the metal plant would find no such reservoir of skills, its start-up costs would be significantly higher. In short, we would have an added inducement for the desired type of company to set up its business.

One environmental obstacle to overcome is the slackness in standards characteristic of areas with a relative over-supply of labor. Such an atmosphere engenders an easy-going attitude which avoids working too hard and opposes attempts on the part of management to increase efficiency. It is, in other words, an underdeveloped area's version of the lump-of-labor and spread-the-work fallacies. Any step-up in productivity is viewed as a reduction in job opportunities; even governments oppose this cost-reducing attempt for fear of a resulting increase in unemployment. In West Africa a humorous conspicuous example of this is the "night watchmen"; these men sleep outside European residences or factories, ostensibly to prevent thievery. It is obvious that they could not stop a theft, but, if no such person were present, it seems fairly certain that the house would be entered. The watchman's wage is the insurance—"protection"—against such illegal entry. If they were not thus employed there would also be that many more idle men, perhaps even looking for such dubious means of income. Similarly, locally based companies hesitate to introduce newer and more efficient equipment for fear that labor would be displaced, thus adding to unemployment. As a result, the less efficient production set-ups stay on, lowering efficiency and keeping costs high.

In this respect it is easier to inculcate modern industrial attitudes in a more capitalistic operation. The less intensive firm has many unskilled employees doing simple operations. Their attitudes and productivity are poor, and this can become infectious, but with more mechanized operations this type of labor is less in evidence, and there is a greater presence of mechanics and other indications of the industrialization tempo. The dominance of machinery thus tends to set the work pace, which, in turn, thus influences the attitude of labor; the environment, so to speak, becomes more mechanized, thus conditioning habits and thoughts.

The other obstacle is the need for better operating care and maintenance. The African's treatment of machinery is shocking to the outside observer; machines are often run until they break down, whereas a simple maintenance effort would extend the operating life for many more years. The need for lubrication and frequent overhaul checks must be inculcated if capital is to be used on a large scale at efficient levels.

SOCIAL CONSIDERATIONS

In assessing the contribution of a high capital/labor ratio, consideration must be given to its bearing on the population problem.

West Africa, like most of the underdeveloped world, is undergoing a population explosion. Thus there is the danger of the high birth rate swamping the efforts to raise *per capita* living standards.

In this respect, the emphasis on intensive capitalization lessens the impact of a given volume of investment. The higher the ratio, the fewer jobs associated with a given investment. Thus the income-increasing effect is more limited. As a result, to the extent that population does respond positively to higher incomes, we have limited its growth and thus reduced the subsequent increase in the future labor force. In brief, the fewer the number who get well-paid jobs, the fewer the additional mouths to feed and the fewer the number of future workers who must be provided with jobs.

The point can be illustrated if we assume, as an alternative, an investment in cottage handicrafts. Many more households would be brought within the scope of the investment, and thus many more households would obtain additional money incomes. Since there has been no disturbance to the family arrangements, cultural habits remain undisturbed, and more mouths can now be supported. As a result, the death rate will decline, while the birth rate remains the same or may even increase. Thus the rise in the population is widespread, and soon a vast new addition to the labor force will need jobs.[11]

On the other hand, by concentrating investment efforts on a small sector, the wage impact is greater and more obvious. A "pole" has been created showing the connection between industrialized habits and income improvement. Since capital-intensive operations should produce appreciably higher wage rates, they might serve as incentives to the remainder of the population to accept the urban-capitalistic way of life in order to obtain the accompanying material benefits. This would contrast with the less intensive approach, where the income effect would be much smaller *per capita*, thus lessening the gap between the factory workers and the others in the

[11] Cf. A. J. Jaffe and K. Azumi, "The Birth Rate and Cottage Industries in Underdeveloped Countries", *Economic Development and Cultural Change*, October 1960, p. 62.

population, and greatly reducing the material attractions and incentives to change to this new life.

Moreover, the above-mentioned handicraft solution is costly as well as contrary to long-run objectives. West Africa has little tradition of production on a commercial scale in this sector in contrast to the situation in India. Therefore, a preliminary stage of training would also be required. Yet, should the economy break through and start to industrialize, most of these skills would be undercut by the more efficient machine-produced goods. As a result, a good deal of the money and effort would be wasted over the longer-run.

Capital-intensive investments would also require less executive and administrative personnel, items in desperately short supply in West Africa. The resulting economies of scale permit a greater output per echelon employee. Even now the Civil Services are finding it difficult to staff the various policy-making positions; the addition of a demand from new manufacturing concerns would only add to the problem.

ELASTICITY OF SUPPLY OF CAPITAL

One of the considerations often overlooked in a discussion of the relative merits of intensive vs. extensive capitalization is the influence on the supply of capital. This cannot be taken as fixed. It may well be that a high capital/labor ratio would induce a greater inflow of capital. For one thing, the production process selected would be closer to that in the industrialized capital-exporter's plants, thus lessening adaptation problems. In addition, the lower wage rates of the West African area coupled with the high productivity resulting from the comparable degree of mechanization and thus lower per unit costs of production should result in profit margins that are higher than in the home country.

In the longer run, moreover, the greater the influx of factories, the greater the market, and thus the still further incentive to set up additional plants. As a result, the rate of industrialization is further increased. In brief, the capital/labor ratio becomes a most important determinant of the ability of an area to achieve the desired "take-off".

Market forces will also aid the suggested efforts to attain more intensive investment. In general the foreign firm is expected to pay a wage higher than the opportunity cost which is available from the indigenous firms or in the alternative occupations in agriculture. Thus, for the foreigner, labor costs are higher. Interest costs, in contrast, tend to be somewhat lower. In part this is the policy of the international and quasi-governmental lending institutions; rates on their loans rarely exceed 6 per cent, whereas the local market rates in West Africa may be up to 100 per cent per annum.[12] Furthermore, the foreign firm can draw on capital from either its parent company or sources within the mother country; rates there are usually well below those cited above for West Africa. As a result, by over-valuing labor and under-valuing capital there is the incentive to substitute capital for labor.[13]

The policy recommendations implicit in this argument can be utilized by the local African governments as well as by the foreign investor. Local development corporations should, therefore, when planning their assistance loans and projects, favor the more capital-intensive alternatives. Since much of their funds would come from low-interest sources, such as the International Bank for Reconstruction and Development and its filial organizations, the U.S. Agency for International Development, and the various West European governmental aid schemes, these monies could be channeled to encourage the industrialization process using the more efficient, more capitalized methods. Here, too, the economies of management would come in, since the greater degree of capitalization would reduce the number of projects launched, thus requiring a smaller supply of executive and administrative personnel, a commodity, as mentioned previously, in terribly short supply throughout the area under study.

[12] Cf. J. C. deGraft-Johnson, *African Experiment* (London: Watts, 1958), p. 120.

[13] Cf. J. Tinbergen, *The Design of Development* (Economic Development Institute, International Bank for Reconstruction and Development) (Baltimore: Johns Hopkins University Press, 1958), pp. 39, 50.

From the foreign firm's point of view this more intensive operation is also economical. The larger plant would be able to bear the overhead cost associated with any international operation, for example, the bureaucracy of supervision and reporting back to headquarters that accompanies any overseas operation. The more the African plant resembles its counterpart at home, the less the necessary adjustments, and the fewer personnel that must be added to supervise the new branch.

SUMMARY AND CONCLUSION

Implicit in all that has been discussed is the radical impact on the existing culture. In effect, current attitudes must be destroyed, or greatly modified, as the industrial atmosphere is substituted for the more traditional subsistence-rural way of life. There is the obvious change in work habits and skills, as well as the complexities that would accompany the increased urbanization. But, in addition, there must be a basic shift in philosophy. Management in Africa would have to become aware of the need for constant change, something new in the hitherto static world in which it has existed. It must learn to think in terms of new techniques, new equipment, and constant improvements in efficiency, in order to maintain its competitive position. This is obviously fundamentally different from the old stable world, one in which change was frowned on and the innovator became an outcast. Whether this Westernization requirement for the industrial sphere would also call for an accompanying revolution in the other aspects of daily life—family relationships, education, land attitudes—can only be touched on in this paper. For example, the extended family has meant that the more prosperous are burdened with parasitic relatives. Such an obstacle to the individual's economic ambitions probably must be abandoned. Similarly, the constant trek back to the land to maintain one's claim there, thus assuring the individual of a place to retire, should be terminated because these frequent interruptions tend to weaken the technical aptitudes painfully acquired, often completely, since they may never return to their former position.

The role of operations research can be inferred from this paper's argument. An over-all assessment of the economy is desirable, including the determination of industries best suited for development. Consideration must be given to the relative importance of both agriculture and industry, as well as the necessary accompanying improvements in the country's infrastructure. Once these basic parameters have been established it is then necessary to plan specific projects and their production functions, aiming at the objective of a relatively high capital/labor ratio. This need for an operational research approach should be applied both to short-run and long-run planning.[14]

[14] Cf. H. B. Chenery, "Comparative Advantage and Development Policy", *American Economic Review*, **51**, No. 1, March 1961, p. 25.

13

UNE EXPÉRIENCE D'UTILISATION D'UN MODÈLE DE SIMULATION POUR L'INITIATION D'ÉCONOMISTES DE PAYS EN DÉVELOPPEMENT

A. SOUSBIE

Chef du Service Organisation et Économétrie de la Sogreah, Grenoble

Au cours du 1er semestre 1961, une vingtaine d'économistes de pays en voie de développement vinrent en France pour y effectuer, sous l'égide de l'ASTEF,* un stage qui s'intitulait "Développement Économique Planifié".

Les stagiaires, qui représentaient la plupart des pays d'Amérique Latine et quelques pays du Proche-Orient, se proposaient à la fois de parfaire leur formation d'économistes et d'étudier les doctrines et les techniques de planification économique appliquées en France ou hors de France par des experts français, tant à l'échelon du pays qu'à celui de la région. Ils furent ainsi amenés à rencontrer nombre de spécialistes de l'Administration, de l'Université et du secteur privé, à visiter quelques-unes des réalisations françaises en la matière, et à prendre connaissance de travaux de recherches en cours. En particulier, les organisateurs du stage pensèrent qu'il ne serait

---

* Association pour l'organisation de stages de techniciens étrangers en France. Cette organisation a été créée par la Coopération Technique Française, avec le concours de la plupart des grandes industries du pays.

pas sans intérêt de présenter aux stagiaires la technique de la simulation et ses possibilités d'applications aux problèmes du développement de grands ensembles économiques. Il fut ainsi convenu que l'un des modèles élaborés par l'équipe Économétrie du Département Scientifique de la Sogreah serait aménagé pour pouvoir être utilisé dans une sorte de "Jeu Économique", inspiré des jeux d'entreprise bien connus.

C'est cette expérience—qui nous paraît présenter un certain caractère de nouveauté—que nous allons essayer de décrire. En premier lieu, nous préciserons les objectifs poursuivis. Puis, nous décrirons sommairement le modèle utilisé et l'organisation du jeu. Enfin, nous tenterons de dégager quelques commentaires sur le déroulement de l'expérience et le comportement des stagiaires.

LES OBJECTIFS

En fait, deux objectifs pédagogiques étaient simultanément visés: Le premier était d'enseignement économique. A deux ou trois exceptions près, les stagiaires avaient acquis dans leur pays une certaine expérience de problèmes économiques partiels, c'est-à-dire limités à une zone géographique réduite ou à des branches particulières d'activité. Par le moyen du "jeu économique" qu'on leur proposait, on allait chercher à les mettre en présence de problèmes d'ensemble, où ils se heurteraient à l'impitoyable interdépendance des décisions et des évolutions, mise en lumière par la contraction du temps qui est l'une des caractéristiques essentielles des systèmes de simulation homme-machine. Nous n'insisterons pas sur les propriétés pédagogiques de ces systèmes. Développées par maints auteurs à propos des jeux d'entreprise, elles sont maintenant bien connues, et on les retrouverait ici point par point.

Le deuxième objectif était de montrer aux stagiaires ce qu'est un modèle de simulation, comment il est construit, et comment il peut être utilisé, en soulignant ses particularités par rapport aux autres grandes catégories de modèles. Il s'agissait, entre autres choses, de montrer que si, en théorie, il n'y a pas de limite à la complication du modèle de simulation par découpage de la réalité socio-économique en mécanismes de plus en plus petits dont le calcul réalisera l'assemblage, des limites sont imposées en pratique par des temps (donc des coûts) de calcul qui deviendraient prohibitifs, et par la possibilité de formulation du comportement de ces mécanismes élémentaires, c'est-à-dire par la finesse de la connaissance du milieu considéré. D'où le besoin, pour qui voudrait construire un modèle, d'investigations statistiques différentes de celles qui suffisent à la comptabilité nationale, et d'où également la nécessité d'adapter strictement l'outil (le modèle) au corps de décisions qu'on lui demandera d'éclairer (choix d'objectifs, de politiques, de moyens) en se gardant, lors de l'utilisation, des chausse-trapes de l'interprétation imprudente ou abusive, hors de la portée des hypothèses retenues.

Il a paru aux organisateurs que le maniement d'un modèle unique pendant plusieurs semaines susciterait certainement chez les stagiaires l'examen critique de sa structure et de sa représentativité, et constituerait un support pédagogique mieux adapté à ce deuxième objectif que la simple description d'une gamme de modèles variés.

CHOIX D'UN MODÈLE

Le choix d'un modèle pour une telle expérience se heurtait à deux impératifs partiellement contradictoires.

Tout d'abord, la simplicité. Pour que le jeu soit aisément mis en route, sans une trop longue période d'initiation et sans courir le risque de tâtonnements décevants lors des premières prises de décision, les règles doivent en être facilement assimilables, c'est-à-dire peu nombreuses, d'énoncé bref et clair, et ne mettant en jeu qu'un nombre raisonnable de coefficients et valeurs. Quant au nombre de décisions à prendre à chaque cycle du jeu, s'il est trop important, il exigera de la part des participants un temps de préparation relativement long, qui nuira à la cadence de déroulement de l'expérience. On est ainsi conduit à rechercher un modèle à structure simple, où l'ensemble des agents économiques soit regroupé en agrégats peu nombreux, donc relativement grossiers.

Mais, si la simplicité du modèle conditionne le déroulement facile de l'expérience, la portée démonstrative et pédagogique de cette expérience appellera au contraire un modèle relativement compliqué, puisque l'on cherchera d'une part à montrer la grande "capacité" des modèles de simulation, et puisque l'on essaiera d'autre part de se rapprocher autant que possible de l'expérimentation sur une réalité économique. Ce dernier point est capital. On fera admettre sans difficulté, et sans préjudice de la portée pédagogique du jeu, que le modèle ne représente qu'une économie fictive, à la condition expresse que cette économie reste vraisemblable. Or, si l'on exclut quelques pays pour lesquels on a avancé l'expression "non-développement", il n'existe pas d'économie nationale facilement réductible à un schéma simple.

A vrai dire, le conflit simplicité de maniement contre fidélité de la représentation se présente aussi lorsque l'on cherche à élaborer un modèle de jeu d'entreprise à des fins pédagogiques. Mais il est alors beaucoup plus facile à résoudre car on peut, sans défigurer la réalité, ramener à un nombre restreint de composantes les problèmes de gestion industrielle. Au surplus, cette recherche de "la plus simple expression" est hautement bénéfique sur le plan pédagogique : elle concentre l'attention sur l'essentiel, souvent dissimulé dans la pratique par une foule d'éléments cependant du second ordre.

Nous disposions pour notre expérience d'une quinzaine d'heures réparties sur deux mois, et l'horaire des stagiaires était trop chargé par ailleurs pour qu'on puisse leur demander un travail important entre les séances. Dans ces conditions, l'expérience n'était concevable qu'avec un modèle très simple, et en-deçà sans doute de "la plus simple expression" acceptable d'une économie vraisemblable. Néanmoins, ainsi que nous le verrons plus loin, les objectifs initialement fixés furent atteints de manière assez satisfaisante. Mais nous tenons à souligner ici que c'est en pleine connaissance de cause que nous avons choisi le modèle très simple dont nous allons maintenant donner une description sommaire.

R

LE MODÈLE RETENU

Toute l'expérience se déroule dans un contexte international parfaitement stable. Les prix à l'importation ou à l'exportation, les taux d'intérêt de l'emprunt ou du prêt restent constants. Toutes les transactions avec l'étranger sont mesurées à l'aide du dollar, qui reste stable et qui est égal, au départ, à l'unité monétaire du pays considéré.

A l'intérieur du pays, les agents économiques ont été regroupés de la façon suivante:

Production

Agriculture (production de matières premières pour l'industrie, et de denrées pour la consommation).
Extraction et première transformation.
Biens d'équipement.
Produits industriels de consommation.

Services

Commerce et Services du secteur privé.
Services publics (y compris l'enseignement, qui se divise en enseignement général, enseignement technique agricole, enseignement technique industriel).

Consommateurs

L'ensemble des particuliers est rattaché à un seul et même groupe de consommateurs.

L'État

Il est représenté par les participants. Ainsi que nous le verrons plus loin, il jouit de pouvoirs économiques très étendus.

A chacun des 4 secteurs de production sont évidemment attachées une fonction de production et une fonction de coût, dans lesquelles interviennent notamment la valeur actuelle des équipements et celle, également "actualisée", de l'effort accompli depuis un certain temps dans l'enseignement.

L'État est maître des investissements dans les trois premiers secteurs, qui travailleront toujours à pleine capacité, sous réserve des possibilités d'approvisionnement.

Par contre, le secteur des produits industriels de consommation est doté d'une plus grande autonomie. Il investit autant qu'il le désire par auto-financement, l'État pouvant en outre lui fournir un complément sous certaines conditions. D'autre part, à l'intérieur de certaines limites, le secteur fixe lui-même chaque mois le niveau de sa production ainsi que ses prix, en fonction de sa propre interprétation de la conjoncture.

Les denrées agricoles destinées à la consommation sont toutes écoulées sur le marché intérieur, à un prix qui ne dépend que de la quantité d'argent que les consommateurs ont décidé de consacrer à l'achat de ces denrées. Toutes les autres productions sont exportables sous certaines conditions; inversement, si les productions nationales sont insuffisantes, le recours à l'importation est possible.

En dehors de l'impôt, l'État n'a aucune prise sur le développement des Commerces et Services du secteur privé, lequel est lié au développement de l'activité productrice générale.

Quant aux Services Publics autres que l'Enseignement, leur développement est lié à celui du Revenu National. Les trois catégories d'Enseignement sont sous le contrôle direct de l'État.

Le nombre des consommateurs, c'est-à-dire l'effectif total de la population, évolue selon une loi qui peut se modifier en fonction du revenu national par tête. Quant à la fonction de comportement de l'ensemble des consommateurs, elle est de type classique: la répartition du revenu global disponible entre produits agricoles, produits industriels et épargne dépend du niveau de ce revenu et du rapport des prix agricoles et industriels.

Aucune épargne n'est thésaurisée. L'État se l'approprie immédiatement dans sa totalité. Il l'utilise, conjointement au produit des impôts, douanes, etc. pour faire face à ses propres dépenses de fonctionnement, et pour financer les investissements qu'il a décidés dans les différents secteurs énumérés ci-dessus, plus un secteur "Infrastructures" qui englobe les infrastructures techniques et sociales (autres qu'enseignement). Les investissements en infra-structures interviennent évidemment dans les fonctions de coût des activités productrices. En outre, à un niveau donné d'investissements dans les autres secteurs, doit correspondre nécessairement un niveau minimum d'investissements en infrastructures.

Naturellement, une dépense d'investissement destinée à un secteur donné n'influe sur les fonctions de production et de coût de ce secteur qu'avec un certain retard. Il en est de même pour les dépenses d'enseignement.

Outre le montant des investissements et des crédits pour l'enseigne-ment, déjà mentionnés, l'État a à déterminer les taux d'imposition, les droits de douane, etc. En fait, pour simplifier le travail des partici-pants, et leur éviter des calculs fastidieux, la possibilité leur a été donnée de fixer seulement des seuils (mini et maxi) entre lesquels ils souhaitaient voir s'établir le montant du déficit (ou de l'excédent) budgétaire d'une part, et le solde de la balance extérieure d'autre part. En cas de dépassement de l'un de ces seuils constaté par l'ordinateur en cours de calcul, des actions correctives étaient auto-matiquement déclenchées, qui reproduisaient à peu près celles qu'auraient pu entreprendre l'État dans les mêmes conditions.

Au total, une douzaine de valeurs chiffrées devaient être déter-minées par les participants à chaque cycle du jeu.

ORGANISATION DE L'EXPÉRIENCE

Il a paru opportun aux organisateurs de consacrer la première partie de l'expérience au "jeu" proprement dit, c'est-à-dire à la réalisation du premier objectif (enseignement économique), per-mettant ainsi une mise en contact en quelque sorte indirecte des stagiaires avec le modèle en tant que tel. Autrement dit, cette première partie devait, tout en poursuivant son objectif propre, préparer les participants à recevoir, en fin de stage, l'enseignement relatif à l'établissement et l'utilisation des modèles de simulation.

Dans ces conditions, la première partie se rapprochait beaucoup, par son organisation et son déroulement, d'une session classique de jeu d'entreprise.

En premier lieu fut donnée une description générale de l'état initial du pays représenté par le modèle, ainsi qu'un tableau reproduisant pour les 5 années précédentes l'évolution des principaux postes de la comptabilité nationale et de quelques grandeurs et indices importants (voir en annexe). Le "fonctionnement" économique du pays fut également décrit, c'est-à-dire les domaines de libre comportement* des groupes d'agents, les formes de ces comportements, les liaisons de dépendance ou d'influence entre les groupes. Mais aucune des formules mathématiques utilisées dans le modèle ne fut communiquée: il ne s'agissait évidemment pas de demander aux participants de se livrer aux calculs dévolus à la machine. Par contre, la connaissance d'un petit nombre de valeurs numériques leur était indispensable pour orienter leur action (coefficients de capital, délai d'efficacité des investissements, etc.). Parmi ces valeurs, certaines pouvaient être estimées à partir du tableau d'évolution des 5 années passées. Une liste des autres a été remise aux participants.

Des équipes de 4 ou 5 membres furent ensuite constituées, et l'on demanda à chacune d'elles de se fixer un objectif à atteindre en 25 ans, et de définir une politique économique générale au service de cet objectif (priorité au développement de certains secteurs, recours plus ou moins large au déficit budgétaire, à l'emprunt à l'étranger, etc.).

Il s'agissait enfin, pour chacune des équipes, de réaliser sa politique par une suite d'interventions espacées de 5 ans dans le déroulement du temps fictif. En fait, au début de chaque période quinquennale, chacune des équipes était autorisée à remettre trois ensemble distincts de décisions, à partir desquels la machine électronique effectuait trois calculs d'évolution économique du pays. Le temps élémentaire du calcul, le Δt, était le mois, mais seules les situations de fins d'années

---

* Bien entendu, par libre comportement, il faut entendre ici comportement automatique, c'est-à-dire hors de la portée des participants, pour tous les groupes d'agents autres que l'État. Pour l'État, au contraire, le domaine de libre comportement est celui qui est couvert par les décisions des participants.

étaient communiquées, dans des tableaux identiques à celui qui avait été soumis au début (modèle en annexe). Les participants étaient donc en présence de trois évolutions, entre lesquelles ils avaient à choisir celle qui leur paraissait la meilleure, compte tenu de la politique qu'ils s'étaient fixée. Ce choix étant fait, on supposait cette évolution quinquennale effectivement réalisée et, à partir de son aboutissement, il fallait préparer trois nouveaux ensembles de décisions pour les 5 années suivantes et ainsi de suite.

Les équipes disposaient en moyenne d'une semaine pour étudier les conséquences des trois ensembles de décisions, retenir une évolution, et préparer trois nouveaux ensembles à livrer au calcul. Elles étaient assistées par les animateurs du jeu, au cours de séances hebdomadaires d'une ou deux heures.

Bien entendu, cette première phase de l'expérience s'est terminée par une conférence de synthèse, consacrée à des comparaisons et des commentaires sur les objectifs et politiques choisis, sur le comportement des différentes équipes, leurs méthodes d'approche du problème et de prise de décision, leurs difficultés, leurs résultats.

Quant à la deuxième partie, consacrée aux modèles de simulation, elle devait donner lieu à plusieurs conférences-débats au cours desquelles, partant de l'analyse du modèle utilisé dans le jeu, on se serait progressivement élevé à un exposé général sur la méthode de simulation. Malheureusement, des retards survenus dans le déroulement de la première partie nous ont empêchés de donner à cette série de conférences l'ampleur que nous avions prévue, et cela n'a pas été sans influence sur les résultats.

COMMENTAIRES ET CONCLUSIONS

Les critiques que l'on peut faire à l'organisation et au contenu de cette expérience ne nous échappent pas. Pour éviter la plupart d'entre elles il eût fallu, croyons-nous, pouvoir disposer de beaucoup plus de temps, et cela, nous le savions dès le départ. Si nous avons cependant décidé, en accord avec les organisateurs du stage, de risquer cette tentative, c'est que nous étions convaincus qu'elle serait fructueuse en dépit de ses imperfections.

En fait, le premier objectif fut atteint de manière très satisfaisante. Au début, nos stagiaires eurent beaucoup de mal à se hisser au niveau des problèmes d'ensemble, et il fallut nous résigner à n'obtenir d'eux que des définitions de politiques extrêmement sommaires. Quant aux premières décisions, elles nécessitèrent l'aide des animateurs, en dépit de la présentation préalable aux équipes d'exemples chiffrés.

Le démarrage du jeu s'avéra donc assez difficile, à tel point même que l'on put craindre de voir certains des participants se décourager ou traiter à la légère la suite des opérations. En fait, il n'en fut rien, au contraire. L'intérêt qui commença à se manifester après les premiers tâtonnements ne cessa de croître jusqu'à la fin du jeu. Au sein des équipes, les débats s'animèrent, parfois même se passionnèrent, puisqu'il nous fallut accepter l'éclatement d'une équipe en deux fractions qui s'étaient heurtées en cours d'expérience à une irréductible divergence de politique.

A cause des difficultés éprouvées au démarrage, et des retards qui en résultèrent, toutes les équipes ne parvinrent pas à dérouler les 25 ans initialement prévus. Et cependant, de l'aveu quasi-unanime des stagiaires, le premier objectif fut atteint de manière tout à fait satisfaisante.

Une fois de plus, un système de simulation hommes-machine s'est donc révélé un excellent outil pédagogique, confirmant pleinement les expériences de jeux d'entreprise déjà réalisées. Mais deux remarques s'imposent ici.

Tout d'abord, dans plusieurs pays d'Europe, les jeux d'entreprise ont parfois suscité des critiques sévères qui, il faut bien le reconnaître, n'étaient pas toujours sans fondement. Les "jeux économiques", si l'on tentait de les développer sans que soient réalisées certaines conditions, pourraient encourir les mêmes critiques, voire même un discrédit qui s'opposerait à la généralisation de leur emploi. Et cela nous paraîtrait d'autant plus regrettable que nous sommes convaincus, après des expériences variées d'utilisation de la simulation à des fins pédagogiques, que deux conditions suffiraient à éviter ces critiques. En premier lieu, il faut que le modèle ait été conçu en vue d'un objectif pédagogique précis. En second lieu, il faut que les animateurs de la session soient d'une compétence éprouvée dans la matière à enseigner, et qu'ils soient doués pour l'enseignement. Faute de quoi (et notamment si les animateurs ne sont que de bons spécialistes du calcul électronique) le jeu ne sera qu'un jeu, agréable sans doute, mais d'une utilité discutable, et qu'on ne manquera pas de discuter.

La deuxième remarque a trait à la portée des conclusions que l'on peut tirer de notre expérience de jeu économique. Dans le cadre de cette expérience, le fait, pour les stagiaires, d'appartenir à des pays en voie de développement, n'était qu'une caractéristique accessoire. Leur caractéristique essentielle était de n'avoir que très peu abordé, dans la pratique, des problèmes d'ensemble. Aussi croyons-nous pouvoir affirmer que, dans la mesure où seront respectées les conditions que nous venons d'exprimer, les jeux économiques pourront contribuer efficacement à la formations des économistes, à quelque pays qu'ils appartiennent. Que l'on pense, par exemple, à tout le parti qui pourrait être tiré, en France, d'un modèle construit autour des problèmes de l'équilibre agriculture-industrie. . . .

Sans doute n'est-il pas nécessaire de préciser que, compte tenu du temps qui nous était imparti et de la simplicité du modèle mis en œuvre, nous ne prétendions pas enseigner aux stagiaires comment résoudre les problèmes économiques d'ensemble—si tant est qu'il existe une méthode générale pour le faire. Ce que nous souhaitions provoquer, c'était une prise de conscience, et nous pensons avoir réussi. Était-il possible, dans d'autres conditions, d'aller beaucoup plus loin? Nous en reparlerons dans quelques instants.

La poursuite du deuxième objectif s'est tout particulièrement heurtée, ainsi que nous l'avons déjà laissé entendre, au manque de temps après l'achèvement du jeu. Si nous avons suscité un intérêt certain pour les modèles économiques de simulation, il s'en faut de beaucoup que nous ayons épuisé le sujet, et que nous soyons sûrs d'avoir toujours été compris. Mais ce ne sont là que des défauts particuliers à notre session, et il serait sans intérêt de s'y attarder. Nous allons essayer, par contre, de tirer quelques commentaires de certaines des réactions manifestées par la plupart des stagiaires à l'égard des modèles en général, et de la simulation en particulier.

Mais, puisque nous allons parler modèles, et simulation, il n'est peut-être pas inutile de répondre par avance à une question qui ne manquerait pas d'être posée: Pourquoi l'aléatoire n'était-il pas introduit dans le modèle utilisé?

Il est certain que techniquement, l'insertion de processus aléatoires dans la chaîne de calculs du modèle ne présentait pas de difficulté notable. Initialement, nous avions d'ailleurs pensé apporter au jeu tel que nous venons de le décrire le perfectionnement suivant: une fois effectué par les équipes le choix d'un ensemble de décisions pour une période de 5 ans, au lieu d'entériner l'évolution correspondante (calculée en régime déterminé), nous aurions effectué un nouveau calcul de l'évolution en introduisant des processus aléatoires, et c'est le résultat de ce dernier calcul que l'on eût conservé. L'idée était de rapprocher davantage la position des équipes de celle d'un gouvernement qui, ayant pris des décisions en fonction des prédictions d'un modèle, voit se développer une évolution réelle plus ou moins différente de celle prédite. Nous l'avons abandonnée simplement pour ne pas compliquer l'exercice, et les difficultés éprouvées dès le début par les stagiaires ont montré que nous n'avions sans doute pas eu tort.

Mais cela ne répond évidemment pas à la question, puisque, même dans l'hypothèse de l'introduction de ce calcul supplémentaire, le modèle effectivement utilisé pour le choix des décisions eût été déterministe.

Il ne saurait être question d'ouvrir ici un débat qui déborderait le cadre de cet exposé. D'aucuns nous reprocheront sans doute d'employer le terme de simulation pour désigner autre chose que la reproduction de phénomènes aléatoires. C'est une pure question de définition, que des instances autorisées trancheront peut-être un jour. A la Sogreah, où nous utilisons depuis longtemps des modèles physiques et mathématiques pour étudier des phénomènes de natures assez diverses, nous nous rangeons jusqu'à nouvel ordre du côté de ceux qui appellent simulation toute reproduction, analogique ou numérique, de l'évolution (aléatoire ou non) d'un système dans le temps.

Savoir si l'on doit ou non faire intervenir l'aléatoire dans un modèle donné revient à savoir si, pour le but visé et compte tenu de l'alourdissement des calculs, le système à représenter doit ou non être considéré comme soumis à des phénomènes aléatoires, et il n'y a évidemment pas là de règle générale.

Dans le cas particulier où il s'agit de tester sur un modèle des politiques économiques à long ou moyen terme pour l'ensemble d'un pays, l'importance des calculs est telle, que le travail sur l'aléatoire, avec les nombreuses répétitions qu'il exige, nous paraît devoir être exclu. Dans l'état actuel des choses nous croyons qu'il faut se limiter à un petit nombre de cycles de calculs pour chacune des politiques à tester, le premier utilisant les valeurs moyennes, les autres faisant intervenir quelques combinaisons, judicieusement choisies par l'opérateur, de valeurs extrêmes des variables aléatoires importantes.

Cette mise au point a sans doute paru superflue à ceux qui pensent comme nous, et elle n'a certainement pas convaincu les autres. Répétons-le, il ne s'agissait pas d'ouvrir un débat, mais simplement de préciser que c'est de propos délibéré que nous avons mis entre les mains des stagiaires un modèle déterministe.

Il est temps maintenant de commenter quelques-unes des réactions que nous avons enregistrées.

Notre première surprise a été de constater combien la notion de modèle, et en particulier de modèle dynamique, était peu familière à la plupart des stagiaires. Et ce n'est pas sans difficulté que nous avons pu les convaincre de ce que le modèle qu'ils manipulaient était tout autre chose qu'un classique tableau d'échanges intersectoriels.

Une autre difficulté—mais celle-là, nous l'avions prévue—a été de montrer en cours de jeu pourquoi et surtout comment le caractère opérationnel devait l'emporter sur le caractère descriptif lors de l'élaboration du modèle. Et, lors des nombreuses occasions qui nous ont été données de parler des investigations statistiques, nous avons pu vérifier à nouveau que moins on a fait ou utilisé de statistiques, plus on est optimiste quant à leur facilité d'établissement et d'emploi.

En ce qui concerne l'emploi des modèles, nous avions à montrer qu'ils peuvent être des outils d'expérimentation. A partir de la possibilité qui avait été donnée aux stagiaires d'essayer trois ensembles de décisions à chaque cycle quinquennal, il nous a été facile de généraliser, et de décrire comment, utilisé de façon beaucoup plus poussée, un modèle pouvait permettre d'essayer des politiques. C'est là pourrait-on dire, de l'expérimentation au premier degré: celle qui est simplement destinée à éclairer l'action. Reste l'expérimentation destinée à parfaire la compréhension.

Selon L. Couffignal, le modèle, système *analogue* à l'original, dont il possède certains caractères sans en posséder tous les caractères connus, a pour but de *faire apparaître des analogies* avec son original, qu'il n'a pas reçues par construction.

Il est bien certain que le modèle de simulation, grâce à sa propriété fondamentale d'assembler des systèmes élémentaires, se prête particulièrement bien à cette recherche d'analogies. Mais une question peut se poser—et quelques petites difficultés survenues au cours de notre jeu nous ont conduits à nous la poser: quelles peuvent être la portée et les limites d'expériences comme la nôtre, utilisant des modèles économiques dont l'original est imaginaire?

Il serait sans doute prématuré de prétendre répondre définitivement à cette question. Mais on peut essayer de formuler quelques remarques, à titre provisoire.

Très grossièrement, on peut ranger en deux catégories les objectifs pédagogiques susceptibles d'être assignés à des expériences de simulation du type hommes-machine: ou bien on veut enseigner un comportement, une méthode de travail, ou bien on veut faire découvrir certaines lois ou caractéristiques propres au système (ou à la catégorie de systèmes) représenté par le modèle. Par exemple, des jeux d'entreprise ont été organisés pour initier des dirigeants à l'emploi d'un "tableau de bord", d'autres pour les conduire à analyser, du point de vue économétrique, les problèmes de régulation de la production et des stocks. Les deux objectifs ne sont d'ailleurs pas exclusifs l'un de l'autre, parfois même ils sont liés. Mais ceux de la deuxième catégorie, qui relèvent de l'expérimentation pour la compréhension, se heurtent à quelques difficultés particulières dans le cas de modèles à original imaginaire.

En fait, dans ce cas, on peut dire que l'on a deux originaux. Seul, le premier, l'original apparent, est imaginaire, et il est identique au modèle. Dans notre jeu, cet original était un pays sous-développé fictif. Construisant à la fois l'original et son modèle, on s'efforce de leur donner le maximum de vraisemblance. Mais on cherche en même temps à obtenir un système dont le comportement soit analogue à celui d'une catégorie de systèmes réels, et c'est cette catégorie qui est le véritable orginal. Par exemple, il s'agissait dans notre expérience de faire découvrir aux stagiaires quelques liaisons d'interdépendance entre certaines variables importantes dans les économies sous-développées.

Réaliser cette analogue pour l'essentiel du comportement est chose relativement aisée pour qui possède quelque habitude de la construction des modèles. Par contre, ce qui est très difficile, c'est d'éviter que des comportements secondaires, et parasites parce que propres au système imaginaire, ne viennent à un moment donné solliciter l'attention des participants, qui chercheront à les comprendre au détriment de l'objectif visé.

Expliquons-nous, en reprenant la comparaison avec les jeux d'entreprise. Il existe, dans la réalité, des entreprises à structure très simple, presque identiques par conséquent aux modèles que l'on peut utiliser dans des jeux pédagogiques. Si donc, en cours de jeu, le modèle d'entreprise révèle, dans certaines situations particulières non prévues par ses auteurs, des comportements secondaires également imprévus, c'est très probablement que la catégorie d'entreprises simples qui a servi d'original au modèle est douée aussi de ces comportements. S'il faut alors—et les participants l'exigeront presque toujours—s'arrêter sur l'analyse de ces comportements secondaires, on rompra certes le rythme de la session, et l'on perdra une partie du temps que l'on souhaitait consacrer à l'analyse des comportements essentiels. Mais, en revanche, les participants découvriront des caractéristiques supplémentaires des originaux réels du modèle.

Par contre, dans une session de jeu économique comme la nôtre, on ne peut, nous l'avons vu, utiliser que des modèles très simplifiés par rapport aux originaux réels. On risquera alors de voir surgir des comportements secondaires propres à l'original imaginaire (et parfois d'ailleurs d'un grand intérêt pour la recherche) qui pourront nuire à l'efficacité pédagogique de l'opération. Les participants, en effet, ne verront peut-être pas clairement, même si on consacre beaucoup de temps à le leur expliquer, pourquoi certains comportements seulement peuvent être généralisés. A tout le moins, on pourra craindre de les voir considérer comme un vice des modèles ce qui n'est en réalité que la manifestation, à travers des conditions d'utilisation imparfaites, d'une de leurs propriétés les plus intéressantes.

Il va de soi que toutes ces difficultés disparaissent d'elles-mêmes si le modèle est à original réel, et cela nous conduit à la conclusion suivante :

Remarquable outil pédagogique, la simulation doit pouvoir être utilisée efficacement pour l'enseignement économique, mais la portée des modèles à original imaginaire sera probablement limitée, en dehors de la recherche, à l'initiation aux grandes lois générales. Par contre, la simulation doit trouver sa pleine efficacité dans une voie où se mêleront l'enseignement et l'action. Enseigner, par le moyen d'un modèle de simulation, l'économie de leur propre pays à ses responsables à différents niveaux, les faire participer à l'élaboration et au perfectionnement de ce modèle, les habituer à l'utiliser pour éclairer leurs décisions, c'est sans doute l'une des grandes voies du progrès économique. C'est, en tout cas, une nouvelle expérience à tenter, qui sera sans commune mesure avec la modeste tentative qui vient d'être décrite.

Annexe

Tableau d'évolution quinquennale du pays imprimé par l'Ordinateur Électronique, et remis aux participants à chaque cycle du jeu.

Résultats du Plan d'Expérience   301 Equipe: 2

		PRODUIT INTÉRIEUR N				
Aux prix courants	Agriculture	5300	5250	5526	5904	6261
	Industrie extractive	358	356	367	377	388
	Industrie manufacturière	3208	3358	3750	3883	4137
En millions d'unites	Equipement-énergie	997	1041	1147	1250	1357
monétaires	Commerce-administration	5737	5868	6070	6291	6501
	Total	15601	15873	16860	17706	18645

		FORMATION NETTE DE CAPITAL				
Aux prix courants	Agriculture	97	223	220	203	192
	Industrie manufacturière	18	199	132	153	112
	Industrie extractive	30	29	20	11	4
En millions d'unites	Equipement-énergie	66	249	222	205	186
monétaires	Total	211	700	594	572	495

		RECETTES ET PAIEMENTS DE L'ÉTAT				
Aux prix courants	Impots sur le revenu	3302	3323	3405	3730	3949
	Impots sur les benefices	272	253	250	262	281
	Impots indirects	961	951	973	1037	1073
	Douane	59	41	46	9	58
	Total recettes	4594	4568	4674	5038	5361
	Investissements en formation infrastructure sociale	1506	1496	1496	1496	1496
En millions d'unites	Investissements en equipements	1034	1143	1187	1223	1229
monétaires	Depenses administratives	2312	2357	2431	2526	2607
	Total depenses	4851	4997	5114	5246	5333
	Balance extérieure	158	392	299	142	115
	Excedent ou deficit	99 —	37 —	141 —	66 —	87

158	162	165	168	173	Indice de produit national par tête
142	146	148	150	153	Indice de consommation générale par tête
126	127	128	129	130	Indice du niveau d'infrastructure sociale
109	105	113	116	120	Indice des prix de détail

UX COUTS DES FACTEURS

4458	4538	4647	4711	4903	
328	330	331	330	333	Aux prix de 1960
3331	3491	3681	3815	3979	
915	965	1034	1092	1164	En millions d'unites
5258	5598	5366	5422	5407	monétaires
14290	14922	15059	15370	15786	

POPULATION

3040	3002	2974	2934	2899	Agriculture	
875	920	966	1016	1057	Industrie manufacturière	
139	140	142	142	143	Industrie extractive	*En*
208	221	233	245	255	Equipement énergie	*milliers*
1154	1192	1178	1188	1224	Commerce-administration	*de*
13510	13626	13741	13856	13969	Total	*personnes*
8106	8176	8245	8313	8382	Inactifs	

TRANSACTIONS EXTÉRIEURES

489	389	436	522	634	Excédent d'exportation de matières premières	
20	13	12	2	9	Excédent d'importation de biens de consommation	*En*
611	738	698	646	527	Excédent d'importation d'equipements	*millions*
101	128	158	181	192	Balance des revenus	*de*
243 −	491 −	432 −	306 −	94 −	Balances	*dollars*
1805	2344	2824	3150	3250		

MONTANT DE LA DETTE EXTÉRIEURE

14

DIFFICULTÉS D'APPLICATION DES TECH-NIQUES MODERNES D'ORGANISATION ET GESTION SCIENTIFIQUES DANS LES PAYS EN VOIE DE DÉVELOPPEMENT

A. SERRA RAMONEDA

Professor, Department of Economics, University of Barcelona

QUAND on pense aux résultats spectaculaires souvent obtenus avec l'application des techniques modernes de gestion dans les pays plus avancés, et notamment aux États-Unis, il est difficile de pouvoir expliquer l'indifférence ou même la méfiance que montrent envers elles les entrepreneurs et chefs d'entreprises des pays qui n'ont pas la chance d'appartenir au groupe de ceux que l'on pourrait appeler de première ligne quant au progrès économique, comme l'Amérique, la Grande-Bretagne, la France, l'Allemagne, la Belgique, etc. Avec une certaine nostalgie, nous avons tous entendu parler des milliers et même millions de dollars que certaines entreprises américaines ont pu libérer et investir ailleurs, grâce à l'application des plus modernes techniques de gestion des stocks, et les réductions de coûts, presque fabuleuses, qu'ont permises des études économiques très perfection-nées. Pourquoi, il est logique de se demander, ces techniques ne sont pas utilisées et ne font pas l'objet d'une demande pressante dans tous les pays qui ne peuvent pas être compris dans le premier groupe des nations situées sur le fer de lance du progrès économique?

Et cependant, il est évident que, d'un point de vue social ou général, l'application de ces techniques est plus pressante et plus nécessaire dans les pays moins développés. Les sociétés opulentes, selon l'expression du professeur Galbraith, pourraient se permettre le luxe de gaspiller des ressources, de ne pas obtenir d'elles les meilleurs résultats, avec une diminution presque imperceptible de leur niveau de vie déjà très élevé. Au contraire, les sociétés moins fortunées devraient utiliser au maximum toutes leurs ressources pour arriver à obtenir un minimum vital de subsistance. Mais il n'en est pas ainsi, et on comprend jusqu'à quel point il serait souhaitable de voir cette situation actuelle, sinon renversée, tout au moins améliorée.

Si d'un point de vue social, il serait urgent de modifier cette situation, il semble que cela devrait l'être aussi du point de vue des entrepreneurs des pays peu développés. Après tout, ce sont les propres entreprises, et donc les entrepreneurs, qui touchent directement les bénéfices résultant de l'application de ces techniques modernes de gestion. Et cependant, ces entrepreneurs ne semblent pas enthousiasmés par les "Management Sciences". La recherche des causes de cette situation est donc importante et intéressante, quoique la réponse à la question posée plus haut ne soit pas aussi simple que l'on pourrait croire au premier abord et que, d'ailleurs, la situation diffère dans chacun des pays si grossièrement réunis sous la commune dénomination de sous-développés. Il est donc hasardeux de donner une réponse unique avec trop de prétentions de précision.

Il est vrai que le caractère de ces techniques, et en particulier la profonde évolution qu'elles sont encore en train de subir, explique en partie l'ignorance dans laquelle elles sont tenues, quoiqu'on puisse établir de profondes différences entre les pays quant au développement. Mais il ne l'explique qu'en partie, car, en premier lieu, dans de nombreux cas, il existe des spécialistes avec des connaissances suffisantes, et, en second lieu, d'autres découvertes et conquêtes scientifiques ont connu une expansion et une diffusion plus rapides, parce que leur utilité était plus facile à apprécier. Tel est le cas de la médecine ou de la technologie industrielle.

Il est sûr, et démontrable, que les chefs d'entreprise des pays sous-développés n'ont pas accordé un grand intérêt à l'utilisation

s

des techniques comprises sous la dénomination de "Management Sciences". Les raisons en sont diverses.

Tout d'abord, il y a une raison de mentalité, d'inertie même. Les entrepreneurs de ces pays ont tiré, en général, et tirent encore des bénéfices très attrayants de leurs activités sans appliquer aucune de ces techniques, faisant confiance en fait à leur intuition. Puisqu'ils ont réussi, du point de vue financier, ils en déduisent que l'intuition est un instrument parfait et ils ne désirent pas changer et ne voient pas la nécessité de le faire. Il y a aussi une question de formation. Notre arsenal de techniques fait souvent appel à des mathématiques très compliquées, à des termes si "suspects" comme utilité ou ophélimité, qu'il échappe à la compréhension des chefs d'entreprises des pays peu développés qui ont, la plupart, une formation purement pratique. Cela n'est qu'un inconvénient mineur, car ils peuvent toujours faire appel à des spécialistes, mais ce qui arrive est qu'ils ne comprennent pas ou doutent de l'utilité d'avoir recours à eux. Car il est évident que, d'une part, il faut connaître un peu ces techniques pour comprendre leurs possibilités et limitations, et, d'autre part, il est difficile de démontrer l'existence d'une relation simple et directe de cause à effet entre l'application de ces techniques et le bénéfice que l'entreprise retire de leur application. En général, le profit d'une entreprise est le résultat d'un ensemble trop nombreux de facteurs pour qu'on puisse l'attribuer exclusivement à l'un d'eux.

Mais ce ne sont pas uniquement des facteurs d'ordre psychologique ou de formation qui rendent difficile l'application de ces techniques par les entrepreneurs des pays sous-développés. Il y a aussi des raisons, et elles sont les plus difficiles à combattre, qui dérivent de la structure économique et sociale caractéristique de ces pays.

Primo: normalement, le manque de capital fixe, l'absence de concurrence, l'inexistence ou presque du processus dynamique que Schumpeter a génialement qualifié de "creative destruction" font que les profits des entreprises sont très importants, puisqu'ils contiennent du "bénéfice de monopole". C'est-à-dire que, dans ces pays, la rentabilité moyenne ou la proportion des profits dans le chiffre d'affaires sont beaucoup plus élevées que les mêmes relations calculées pour les entreprises américaines travaillant dans les mêmes secteurs industriels. Il est alors compréhensible que, devant l'importance de ces profits, les entrepreneurs ne fassent pas trop d'efforts pour réduire les coûts industriels et, en dépit de ce que dit la théorie économique sur l'entrepreneur rationnel, que l'utilité qu'ils pourraient obtenir avec l'application des "Management Sciences" sous la forme d'un accroissement relativement petit des profits ne compense pas la désutilité provoquée par le travail, les préoccupations et les dépenses qu'entraînent les études économiques.

On peut en plus observer que, *ceteris paribus*, les entrepreneurs préfèrent, dans ces pays, concentrer leurs efforts sur les questions fiscales et même politiques. Généralement, les systèmes fiscaux de ces pays sont imparfaits, sans parler de la qualité de l'Administration fiscale, et laissent des portes ouvertes par où il est possible d'évader les charges fiscales, soit moyennant une utilisation intelligente des lacunes légales soit grâce à des moyens moins avouables.

Également, les questions politiques, tout au moins de politique économique quand elles touchent la branche d'activité des chefs d'entreprise, semblent avoir un intérêt important. Dans les pays qui nous occupent, le pouvoir économique est normalement concentré, de même que le pouvoir politique, mais de façon plus occulte. Si donc les entreprises arrivent à dominer et à modeler la politique économique, les bénéfices sont gigantesques. Je pense en ce moment aux exemptions fiscales, primes d'exportation, salaires officiels, contrats du gouvernement, etc.

Il est donc normal que, étant donné cette structure, les chefs d'entreprise n'aient que très peu d'intérêt pour toutes les nouvelles techniques d'organisation et gestion scientifiques. Il est compréhensible et logique que les entrepreneurs, qui, par définition, cherchent le bénéfice, le fassent par la voie la plus courte et la plus facile.

Secundo: il est vrai que l'arsenal des nouvelles techniques a moins d'efficacité dans les pays sous-développés. Effectivement, les données sont insuffisantes, les statistiques sont inexistantes ou tout au moins douteuses. Et on sait combien ces données sont importantes pour l'application efficace de certains modèles. Avec le manque d'information, l'utilité des "Management Sciences" décroît. En plus, l'instabilité politique qui souvent règne dans ces pays et, en tout cas, les changements brusques, inattendus, et le manque de continuité des objectifs de la politique économique n'encouragent pas les entrepreneurs à faire des plans à trop long terme. Il faut reconnaître que l'horizon économique se rétrécit au fur et à mesure que l'on descend le long de l'échelle du développement économique. Tout se fait de façon plus provisoire et plus impulsive.

De tout ce qui précède, on peut tirer les conclusions suivantes. Il paraît évident que nos techniques ont un rôle très important à jouer dans le développement des pays arriérés. Mais, pour atteindre ce but, il ne suffit pas d'instruire et de créer des spécialistes, de donner des bourses d'études, etc. Cela, en tout cas, ne peut être qu'un premier pas : car si les entrepreneurs ne font pas appel à ces spécialistes, tous ces efforts, toutes ces bourses d'études auront été vains.

Il faut donc utiliser d'autres moyens, afin de faire que les entrepreneurs fassent appel aux spécialistes. Pour cela, il faudrait vaincre en premier lieu les inconvénients d'ordre structurel. Disons que, probablement, le développement économique peut les faire disparaître, et surtout l'expansion du commerce international due en particulier aux accords internationaux et à la création d'unités économiques supra-nationales. Le phénomène est trop connu pour s'y attarder.

Mais, et cela nous vise directement, les moyens qu'il faut utiliser pour vaincre la résistance, l'inertie et l'apathie des entrepreneurs concernent :

(a) l'éducation des chefs d'entreprise, non pas comme spécialistes, mais comme personnes comprenant les possibilités offertes par les "Management Sciences". Les Commissions ou Agences nationales de Productivité ont eu un rôle efficace de ce point de vue, parfois un succès extraordinaire, comme en ce qui concerne l'Organisation Scientifique du Travail. Il faut remarquer qu'obtenir le même succès pour les nouvelles techniques de gestion est plus difficile. Elles sont plus abstraites et leurs résultats moins palpables que les techniques propres de l'Organisation Scientifique du Travail. Une visite à une usine américaine, par exemple, met sous les yeux des entrepreneurs des pays arriérés la réduction de main-d'œuvre qu'on peut obtenir grâce à une organisation scientifique du travail. Mais leur faire comprendre les avantages obtenus avec une programmation mathématique de la production ou avec une étude économétrique de la politique de prix n'est pas si facile. Il faudrait donc publier des brochures, donner des conférences, etc. pour mettre en valeur, d'une façon simple et directe, l'utilité des nouvelles techniques de gestion.

(b) la réduction des coûts des études, qui, effectivement, sont trop élevés pour les niveaux des prix des pays. Cela pourrait se faire avec une aide financière de l'État ou des collectivités.

(c) le rôle des entreprises publiques, lesquelles devraient donner l'exemple et créer ou donner du travail aux groupes d'études, et donner de la publicité aux études réalisées.

Cette liste n'est pas complète. Le manque de temps m'empêche de raffiner l'étude des moyens et des inconvénients. Mais ce que je tiens à souligner est l'importance et la nécessité de faire utiliser les nouvelles techniques par les pays arriérés. Pour développer un pays, il ne suffit pas d'établir de nouvelles entreprises, avec un outillage très moderne, et d'importer de grands calculateurs électroniques. De la même façon que l'utilisation efficiente des armes modernes exige la création au sein de l'armée de groupes de Recherche Opérationnelle, tous ces outillages, tous les calculateurs exigent, si l'on veut extraire d'eux un maximum de rendement, l'application des nouvelles techniques. Sans cela, l'addition de nouveaux équipements et l'augmentation du capital réel n'impliquent un développement économique que si l'on introduit et utilise également le "know-how". Et ce "know-how", évidemment, ne se limite pas aux seules connaissances technologiques pour faire fonctionner le capital réel; c'est tout un état d'esprit.